W9-CAO-243

HOW I WON THE WAR

How

Lieutenant Ernest Goodbody

1964 · William Morrow & Company/New York

I Won the War

as told to PATRICK RYAN

Second Printing, December 1964

Copyright © 1963 by Patrick Ryan.

Published in Great Britain in 1963.
Published in the United States in 1964.

Printed in the United States of America.
Library of Congress Catalog Card Number 64-7885

This book is dedicated to all who served
under my command in the Second World War,
to that happy band of brothers in arms who
hit the Boche for six all the way from the
Mediterranean to the Baltic, to Twelve
Platoons, the Fourth Musketeers.

Ernest Goodbody
Lieutenant

ACKNOWLEDGEMENTS

The following is a list of titles from which the extracts used as chapter headings in this book were taken. The author gives his grateful thanks to the respective authors and publishers who gave their permission for these quotes to be used.

AS HE SAW IT by Elliot Roosevelt. Copyright 1946 by Elliot Roosevelt. (Reprinted by permission of Duell, Sloan & Pearce, New York.)

THE BUSINESS OF WAR by Major-General Sir John Kennedy. (William Morrow & Co.)

CAMPAIGN IN ITALY by Eric Linklater. (Her Majesty's Stationery Office.)

CRUSADE IN EUROPE by General Dwight D. Eisenhower. Copyright 1948 by Doubleday & Company, Inc. Reprinted by permission of the publisher.

DEFEAT INTO VICTORY by Field-Marshal Sir William Slim. Reprinted by permission of David McKay Company, Inc.

ECLIPSE by Alan Moorehead. (hamish Hamilton Ltd.)

ESCAPE TO ACTION by Lt. General Sir Brian Horrocks. Copyright 1961. Reprinted by permission of St. Martin's Press, Inc. (Published in England under the title, A FULL LIFE, William Collins Sons & Co., Ltd.)

GALLANT GENTLEMEN by E. S. Turner. (Michael Joseph Ltd.)

HANDBOOK OF MILITARY LAW by General Sir Charles Harrington (W. Clowes & Sons Ltd.)

HITLER and HIS ADMIRALS by Anthony Martiennsen (Secker & Warburg Ltd.)

MEMOIRS OF FIELD-MARSHALL MONTGOMERY by Viscount Bernard L. Montgomery. Copyright 1958. Reprinted by permission of World Publishing Co.

WAVELL: PORTRAIT OF A SOLDIER by Brig. Bernard Fergusson. (William Collins Sons, Ltd.)

[vii]

The experiences described in pages 19-23, 176-81 and 193-4 have already been reported in *JOHN O' LONDON'S, PUNCH* and *COURIER* respectively.

HOW I WON THE WAR

Chapter One

"It is quite unbelievable," wrote Brooke, "that things should have gone so well to date. It is a great gamble for a great stake and I pray God that it may come off." Despite the inexperience of the landing-craft crews it came off next morning almost beyond expectation. At 1 a.m. on November 8th, 1942, the troops began to go ashore on the Algerian beaches. . . .

SIR ARTHUR BRYANT
War Diaries of F.-M. Viscount Alanbrooke

As far as I could see along the beach there was chaos. Landing-craft were beaching in the pounding surf, broaching to the waves, and spilling men and equipment into the water. Men wandered about aimlessly, hopelessly lost, calling to each other, swearing at each other and at nothing. There was no beach party or shore party anywhere in sight. I was chilled. . . . I was lonely . . .

GEN. L. K. TRUSCOTT
Command Missions

As THE LANDING CRAFT pitched into the breakers, a taste of verdigris queased into my throat. Blanco puffed up from the gas mask on my chest and desiccated my mouth. That steel helmet was murdering my skull. I felt distinctly unwell, but it would never do to let the chaps see it. A commander must never show weakness in front of his troops.

I swallowed cavernously and gave Sergeant Transom a heartening slap on the shoulder.

"Well, Sergeant, here we go then," I said. "Getting our chance at last of a good old crack at the Boche, eh?"

[1]

He lowered his binoculars, surveyed me gloomily for some seconds, and spat silently into the sea. Grand chap in a tight corner, Transom, but not overarticulate.

With four hundred yards to go we ran into the low morning mist which skeined along the Algerian coast. The ramp came down to half-mast and I judged it time to read the Order of the Day. It was a noble, rousing message the general had penned, just the thing to give the chaps that final lift up the beach. I took the card from my map case and moved forward to the slope of the ramp.

"Men of the Fourth Musketeers," I declaimed, "we go forth together on this historic day, the eighth of November 1942, to embark on a Great Adventure. We invade Algeria to do our bit in defence of the Old Country, the Empire and the Democratic Way of Life. Let us go into the ring for this first round with the Light of Battle in our eyes and the Strength of Righteousness in our hearts. If we all pull together with true British pluck and team spirit, we shall, with the support of the Almighty God of Battles, win His just victory over the Forces of Evil. . . . Good luck to you all, good hunting and tally-ho! to kick the Hun for six out of Africa!"

"And up the Spurs!" shouted Private Drogue.

"I would also add just a few personal words of my own . . ."

Before I could do so there was a grinding crunch below the waterline, the nose of the craft slid skywards, the ramp shot away from under my feet and pitched me backwards into the Mediterranean. I bumped rock and old iron six feet down and came to the surface with the tide carrying me already ten yards away from my command. The mist swirled down, but I could still make out the rearing shape of the boat and hear the engines roaring madly.

As I drifted farther away my feet touched sand and I was able to stand against the race. I blew my whistle and put my right hand on top of my head in the approved signal laid down in the *Infantry Training Manual*.

[2]

"Rally!" I shouted. "Rally! Number Twelve Platoon, the Fourth Musketeers, rally on me!"

Three times I gave this order, but nobody came to look for his commander. At first I could not understand. I undoubtedly had the affection of my men. Man-management had ever been my abiding interest. I had advised each of them at length about his marital affairs, arranged compulsory saving of a sensible part of their pay and never taken my meal on exercises until they had eaten. Sometimes they ate the lot and there was none left for me. Sergeant Transom, though admittedly lacking in imagination, was a most loyal N.C.O., and we had been together for a long time.

As the craft went astern and out of sight I realized that my abandonment was a naval decision. Underwater obstructions had been encountered and another approach must be found. My chaps would have come for me if they could. But the Navy was in command. A good chap, too, that sub-lieutenant. When I took him through the details of my Beach Landing Programme he had shown, for an untrained naval officer, a surprisingly intelligent appreciation of Army problems, and I had told him so.

The sound of the engines died away and I was alone and unsupported, neck-deep in the warm lopping sea.

"Now, steady, Ernest," I said to myself. "Steady up and remember Clausewitz."

It has ever been my custom in any military dilemma to make a quick appreciation of the situation based on Clausewitz's *Principles of War*. The commandment appropriate to my present circumstances was clearly "Maintenance of the Objective." Not only would this action get me on to dry land, but it might also bring me back to my platoon.

Urged on by the tide, I strode through the shallows and found myself in a tiny cove framed by low red cliffs. Somewhere over the top and a mile inland lay our first bound, the village of Cleptha. My beach seemed deserted, and I only

[3]

hoped that if Sergeant Transom met opposition he would remember my battle plan. It was an adaptation of the Montgomery left-hook technique and needed a mathematical mind to apply it at platoon level.

The mist lifted and the sun came through as I crawled over the sand and up onto the rise of the dunes. I was steaming like a frosty scrum when I reached the rocks below the crest. . . . There was a sudden clatter of stones above me and a man came running out onto the ridge.

He looked like an Arab, dressed in brown folk weave with an antimacassar around his head. But you could never be too careful. Damned crafty, the Hun. So I dived for cover and landed in a bed of thistles.

"Halt!" I commanded. "Who goes there?"

The lanyard of my revolver tangled in my entrenching tool and I couldn't get my weapon out. Fortunately, my adversary stopped ten feet away. I caught the full smell of him down wind and knew he couldn't be a German.

"O.K., Johnnie," he piped. "Hurrafor King George."

I had my pistol unravelled now and kept him covered as I came into the open.

"You speak English?"

"O.K., Johnnie. Hurrafor King George."

He turned back the way he had come and beckoned me to follow him.

"That way?" I asked. "Cleptha?"

"Cleptha. O.K., Johnnie. Hurrafor King George." He nodded triumphantly and pointed to himself, "Momali . . . Momali."

If the landing is unopposed, said our orders, make immediate contact with the civil authorities. This was my chance. My landing was unopposed. Here was a guide. If I contacted the local headman the place would be my personal, bloodless victory. The major would be delighted.

"Take me to your sheikh," I commanded. He jumped twice in the air in delight and went flap-footing down the track. Once away from the sea, the wind blew hot and dry and the worst of the wet was out of me when, after twenty minutes' trot, we came to the mud-brick and corrugated-iron outskirts of Cleptha. White houses sprang up as we hit the high street, a pavement, then shops, cafés, the market-place and the mosque. Arabs stood up and clapped us through as though we were finishing the marathon. One ran alongside and grabbed my arm. Momali kicked him *à la savatte* and sent him spinning into a barrow of dried octopi. We reached a two-story house with green shutters and flags of all nations decorating the balcony. Momali shepherded me between potted palms and into a tiled hall dripping with bead curtains.

A fat, swart woman with two Union Jacks topping her Madame Butterfly chignon came whooping through the beadwork. In a torrent of molten French and a smother of eau-de-Cologne, she folded me in her vast bosom and kissed me violently on either cheek, leaving gouts of lipstick to mark her passage. She bore me down into a raffia armchair and pushed a hassock under my feet.

"Momali," I asked. "This lady. She wife of the sheikh?"

"O.K., Johnnie. Hurrafor King George." He nodded vigorous agreement and flapped off back into the street.

My hostess rang a cowbell and a boy brought in coffee and a bottle of Rule Britannia A¹ Scotch Whisky. There was giggling above me and a dozen young women of various shades and sizes looked down from the gallery at the top of the stairs. I was getting the hang of things now. Butterfly was the sheikh's No. 1 Wife and the others were the junior members of his harem. It was customary, no doubt, for the No. 1 Wife to offer hospitality before a guest met her master. She poured me a glass, half coffee, half Rule Britannia. Like Montgomery, I do not normally take alcohol but this was clearly in the line of political duty. I drank and the first gulp dried out my vest.

No. 1 screamed at the other wives and they came down the

stairs and paraded like mannequins before my chair. I smiled politely and drank a little fire-cocoa to each in turn. All part of the welcoming ceremony, I thought, until I realized that Butterfly, in basic French and all too obvious sign language, was inviting me to choose one for my carnal pleasure.

I had heard tell of the magnitude of Arab hospitality, but this was old-world courtesy run mad. How could you possibly negotiate politically with a man ten minutes after you'd been up to all sorts with one of his wives? Besides, I've never been a chap for that sort of thing. I was not, thank God, brought up promiscuous.

A wet-lipped wife in a strained kimono sat down on my knee and I swallowed the rest of my coffee for safety. Her hands wandered everywhere and left me in no doubt as to her eagerness to sacrifice herself in the name of hospitality. It was a good thing I'd kept my equipment on.

"Non, madame," I said. *"Merci beaucoup, mais non."*

She took this disclaimer for shyness and I was struggling with her in defence of British military honour when there came a wild shouting from the street and Momali, followed by Sergeant Transom and Twelve Platoon, rushed in.

No. 1 Wife burst her stays in a torrent of delight, all the other wives ran upstairs and the platoon went after them.

"Well," said Sergeant Transom, "but you soon got on the old job, didn't you?"

"I am here to negotiate with the sheikh," I said. "Momali led me to his house. We must see that he is rewarded."

"He's been rewarded. Best day's commission ever earned by any Algerian brothel-runner."

Butterfly took a wash leather bag from her cleavage and counted a pile of coins into Momali's wriggling palm. A small bush fire ran up the back of my neck.

"You mean, Sergeant . . . that this is nothing but a . . . but a disorderly house?"

[6]

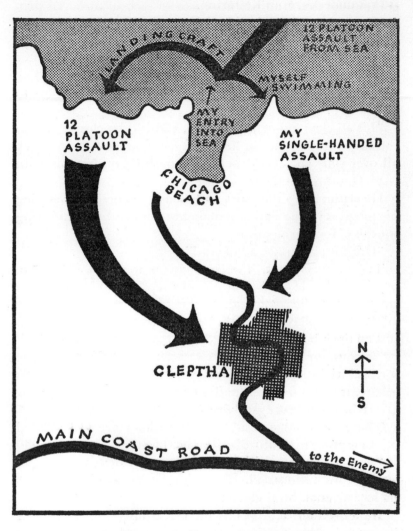

The Capture of Cleptha—November 1942

I had not been in such a place before. All that sort of thing is kept under cover in Kettering.

"Don't come the old acid with me, sir. You're a dark horse all right. All them lectures about leave the Wog tarts alone and here you are not landed five minutes and straight after a bit of Algerian under."

"Now, Sergeant Transom, I want to make it quite clear to you that . . ."

"It's all clear enough to me, sir, and it'll be clearer still to the major if he comes in here and sees you with that lipstick all over your gob. We'd better be pushing on for the main road. Out through the back door, too."

He clattered up the stairs and along the corridor, marking his progress by the slap of female buttocks and the answering squeals of foreign anguish.

"Outside on parade, all of you!"

Ten minutes later, Twelve Platoon was back in action, moving in battle formation out of Cleptha and up a sunken track towards the coast road.

"Roll on, bleeding death," said Private Spool. "We was just on the job lovely when he has to have everybody out."

"In, out, on guard," said Private Drogue. "All I had time for. All right for him, mind you, crafty perisher. Swims ashore, nips up smartish and gets in a couple of long, slow grinds before we ever get there."

There was a tinge of admiration in his voice so I decided not to reprove him. More serious matters took my attention.

"Sergeant Transom," I said. "We're not observing proper anti-gas precautions. The leading man has no litmus paper on his bayonet."

He looked down at the thick, white dust puffing over our boots.

"Nor he hasn't, sir," he said in surprise. "And this is a dead likely place to meet mustard gas, and all. I'll see to it right away."

[8]

He moved forward and spiked a sheet of paper on Private Drogue's bayonet.

"What we on now," asked the gas sentry. "Flag day?"

The litmus paper did not look of standard size to me and so I went up to inspect. It was a square of toilet paper. Quite useless, I assure you, for detecting mustard gas deposits. I was about to remonstrate with the sergeant when I noticed that no one in the platoon but myself still had a gas mask. They'd all thrown them away. This was too grave a matter to be dealt with on the line of march. We would have to have a kit inspection on the objective.

Steadily we plodded up the track and as we breasted the final rise we came in sight of the black ribbon of the road. I squared my shoulders and moved forward with the point section to lead my men in the final assault. A great exultation flowed over me. . . . Everything I had been through was suddenly worth while. . . . The sacrifice of my corn-chandling career, those tough months in the ranks, the merciless grind of O.C.T.U. training, the endless nights of military study, the digging, the drilling, the cross-country runs, the E.N.S.A. concerts, the A.B.C.A. lectures, the V.I.P. parades, the cleaning of snow, the polishing of coal, the whitewashing of stones and all the thousand hammer blows that went to forge a soldier fit for twentieth-century war . . . all were proudly justified in this crowning moment as I marched forward with my men in the Spearhead of Democracy. And, as the African sun aimed arson on top of my tin hat and twin rivers of sweat coursed down behind either ear, my memory made green again that wet October morning when it all began, two years ago, and I walked into the recruiting depot in High Street, Kettering, plain Mr. Ernest Goodbody, rankless, uncommissioned, an utterly unarmed civilian. . . .

Chapter Two

The unpreparedness of Britain in 1914, when it was the only country in the world whose Army had field-guns incapable of firing a high-explosive shell, was eclipsed by Britain's almost unbelievable lack of fighting material twenty-five years later in 1939. What had been obsolete in 1914 was still in use. . . . We had no sub-machine-guns, no rimless cartridges, no percussion grenades. . . . There were, of course, no dive-bombers in the Air Force and the tanks were fit only for museums. The solar helmets issued to troops going East to defend India, Burma and Malaya were remnants of the South African war. Nearly all the bombs the R.A.F. possessed in 1939 had been left over from 1919. . . . It was never questioned, however, that the British Army's cavalry lances and swords, their saddles, horseshoes, picks, shovels and tent mallets were the equal of any in the world . . .

GEN. SIR LESLIE HOLLIS
War At The Top

I SPENT MY early childhood cowering before that poster of Kitchener's demanding finger and accusative moustache. The outbreak of war brought me nightmares in which beautiful young women handed me white feathers in the street. I was single and unattached and my country needed me. And there seemed little likelihood that corn-chandler's chief clerk would become a reserved occupation.

So, on the last Friday in October 1939, I balanced the lentil ledger, initialled the stock totals and informed Mr. Cawberry that I was rallying to the flag. I must say he took it very well.

"Cawberry and Company have had you for six years, my

boy," he said. "It seems only fair that someone else should have a turn. I trust and hope that in these dark days Cawberry's loss will be the Army's gain."

The drill hall was dim with cold fog and spectrums glowed about the gas lights. Icy-fingered doctors did things to me which I would rather not discuss in mixed company. The clerk at the final table booked me in for posting.

"You are free to choose any arm of the Service you wish," he said, "and provided there are vacancies in that arm and your qualifications are suitable, you will be posted there."

"I've always fancied the Secret Service. M.I.5, you know. Military Intelligence."

"Military Intelligence, eh?" He read aloud as he wrote. "Arm of Service preferred . . . M.I. . . . Right you are. Next please."

I spent the next three days at the library reading up on Mata Hari and on the Monday morning received my orders to report to Burrapore Barracks, the training depot for Motorized Infantry. After counting us all five times, they found they had exactly five barrack rooms full and one man over. I was the odd man out and was marched away to Number Seventeen by Corporal Maloney and Lance Corporal Dodds.

"He's scrawny," said Maloney, eyeing me distastefully, "and dead windy-looking."

"He's all we got," said Dodds, "until the other thirty-nine arrive tomorrow. I hope to Gawd Hitler don't strike to-night."

They instructed me in the art of polishing coal, appointed me fire picket and left me in charge of the barrack room. Sitting there on my first night in the Army, coal in hand and unheroic, looking down a bleak vista of naked bedsteads, I felt lone, lorn, and very Dickensian.

The corporals returned soon after ten, both with a skinful and a quart bottle of the same again, and settled before the fireplace to reminisce. I listened in disciplined silence and gathered that while the chunky corporal was a regular soldier of twenty-four years' unbroken service, his willowy lance jack was a reservist who had been called back to the Colours after five years of civilian life.

Their exchanges developed into a debate about the relative merits of Army and civilian life. Maloney proclaimed his absolute conviction that the Army gave a man the best bargain.

"Free grub, free travel, a place to kip, and the best clobber that money can buy. You don't get no civvy trash in the Army, my boy."

Dodds, speaking from experience of both worlds, was equally convinced that in all things the civilian was superior to the military.

"You just don't know, Paddy," he said. "You ain't sampled civvy stuff like I have."

For answer, Maloney took off his ammunition boots and put them proudly on the table.

"Look at them. Strong as houses, soft as bosoms, and eight years on my feet already. You don't get boots like that in civvy street."

Dodds lugged off his black shoes and planted them beside the boots. He unbuttoned his jacket for comfort and I saw that, underneath his battle dress, his evening wear was civilian throughout.

"Box calf, those are. Six years I've worn them and they're as good as the day I bought them in Leather Lane. You get nothing like them in the Army."

Maloney brushed the shoes contemptuously aside.

"Cardboard and brown paper! A shower of rain and you'll be barefoot." He stripped off his grey socks. "Feel those. Pure wool, they are. There's body in them ..."

"Pure wool is it you're after? Then read what that label says."

Dodds was off with his lovat-mixture civvy socks and stretching them across the table.

"Thin as bloody cobwebs and about as hard wearing." Maloney was already wrestling with his jacket. "Let's see your shirt."

He pulled his khaki shirt over his head and fell down twice before he got out of it.

"Flannel, that's what that is, solid flannel." He cracked his shirt like a stock whip. "What doctors prescribe for the rheumatics and the Army gives it to you free."

"And it scrapes the skin off your shoulders in the first week," countered Dodds, holding out his striped poplin. "Now, there's a shirt for you. A decent civilized piece of clothing for a human being . . ."

And they went on with their partisan strip poker, comparing braces, buttons, handkerchiefs, brushes, combs, vests, and pants until, finally, all their belongings were piled on the table and they were standing naked before me.

"Rotten, threadbare, civvy street muck," jeered Maloney. "Puff o' wind . . . and where are you?"

"Clogs and canvas and crummy great shirts they don't even give to convicts . . ."

Each took a long swig to ease his flow. They gurgled and swayed in the firelight, rosy and paunchy enough for any bacchanal. Given a bunch of grapes and a satyr or two and they'd have had Rubens reaching for his roller. Maloney suddenly slammed down the bottle.

"Teeth!" he yelled. "You can't beat Army teeth."

His hand went up to his mouth and he pulled out a complete top set and laid them glistening on the table.

"Look at those beauties. Made for me by an Army dentist in Quetta. Fitted like a glove, the day I got them. That's quality for you, Dodds . . . quality you'll never get from any civilian . . ."

"Oh! No? . . . Just take a look at these." The lance corporal

[13]

whipped out his own top set and laid them down for inspection. "Hand made those were by Mr. Gravel, the finest dentist in the whole Seven Sisters Road. Pure ivory, them teeth are, not bone and bakelite like those crunchers of yours . . ."

"I'll show you bone and bakelite, I will." Maloney bashed his teeth madly on the edge of the table.

"Hard as iron. Tough as teak. You bash your tombstones like that!"

Dodds crashed his dentures down.

"There you are . . . teethmarks in the wood and not a chip out of them anywhere. That's civvy workmanship for you, Paddy, and they're built to last. . . ."

Maloney solemnly picked up his teeth and hurled them against the wooden wall of the barrack room. They bounced down and scuttered back across the floor like a racing crab.

Dodds slung his teeth overarm and they ricocheted back to him off the beading.

"Not a scratch on mine anywhere," he proclaimed.

"Not a mark on mine neither. That's Army gear for you."

Maloney hurled his set again, Dodds took up the challenge and they settled to a regular fusillade of teeth following teeth in rapid fire against the woodwork. This tattoo, however, brought no decision.

"You ain't throwing yours as hard as me, Dodds."

"I'm throwing flat out. You're pulling your punches because you're afraid of busting your load of plastic. You're just lobbing them up like Granny . . ."

"Am I, indeed? Lct me tell you . . ." Maloney stopped suddenly in mid-tirade and looked at me. "That's it, Dodds . . . him. He's neutral. . . . Hut! Shun! . . . Quick march! . . . Jump to it, boy! . . . Halt!"

I was in my black and red pyjamas with the Russian eagle on the pocket. I forgot I was barefoot and slammed down a halt that sent me hammer-toed.

[14]

"Gawd!" said the naked Dodds. "Rudolph Valentino. All done up for the old business."

"He's neutral," said Maloney. "We'll have him throw both lots at once. That's fair, ain't it?"

He handed me both sets of teeth.

"Throw them false teeth against that wall. Hard as you can."

I freely confess that I was unprepared for this situation. I had braced myself to meet the hardship, horror, and sacrifice of total war, but I had not anticipated that the Army's first direct order to me would be, "Throw them false teeth against that wall." I realized that military orders must be obeyed without question, but some civilian atavism warned me that this way I would make enemies, and I hesitated. What greater insult can you pay a man than to throw his false teeth against a wall?

"Come on, now," growled Maloney. "Get on with it or I'll have you down the guard room for insubordination."

"You sling them teeth when you're told," said Dodds, "or I'll have you up for court-martial."

I reflected that they could shoot you in wartime for refusing to obey an order. I drew back my arm and hurled the two sets of teeth at the wall. Unfortunately, I missed the woodwork and hit the granite surround of the fireplace. The dentures shattered to pieces . . . hailstones of ivory and pellets of coral scattered the barrack room floor, and the holystoned hearth was like the bottom of a dentist's dustbin.

"Me teeth!" moaned Maloney. "You've smashed me beautiful teeth."

"You've broke them," cried Dodds, kneeling down and fingering the rubble. "You bloody Cossack, you . . . you Sheikh of Araby, you've broke my top set completely."

In a smart and soldierlike manner, I stood to attention after my throw, awaiting the next order.

[15]

"I'm very sorry," I said. "But you told me to. I was only obeying your orders."

Maloney was all for beating my teeth out there and then to join his own on the floor. But Dodds, a true barrack room lawyer, restrained him.

"We'll have him up in the morning, Paddy," he said. "He'll get the glasshouse for this. But if you mark him now, he'll plead provocation."

They retired to their cubicles, swearing flabbily and calling down curses on my military career. I was very unhappy and the only consolation I could draw from the situation was that they couldn't bite me.

I was up next day on company orders charged with "Conduct to the prejudice of good order and military discipline in that he deliberately smashed the false teeth of his corporals." Maloney and Dodds said that without even a by-your-leave I took their teeth from the table and hurled them against the fireplace. It took me about twenty minutes to go through the true sequence of events and to explain to the company commander that I had been a neutral tooth-thrower, a pressed arbitrator acting under strict orders.

When I had finished he was clearly uncertain whether I was drunk or barmy. He finally wrote all over my records in red ink, notched me seven days' C.B. (confined to barracks) for luck, told the sergeant major to watch out for me as a potential troublemaker and booked me for an early visit to the psychiatrist.

Chapter Three

Our new armies are to be officered by classes of society who are new to the job. The middle, lower and working classes are now receiving the King's Commission. These classes, unlike the old aristocratic and feudal (almost) classes who led the old army, have never had "their people" to consider . . .

LETTER TO *THE TIMES* FROM
AN O.C.T.U. *Commandant*

WITH THE BUGLE calling me at inconvenient hours, Sergeant Major Grope beady-eyeing me at every turn and two gummy corporals chasing me from pillar to post mumbling toothless, incomprehensible orders, my opening week in the Army did nothing to confirm that a field marshal's baton was hidden in my knapsack. But I did not allow this first misfortune to deter me. I applied myself to my duties with zest, smiling as I polished dustbins, whistling as I whitewashed coal bunkers, laughing aloud as I lathered latrines.

"If yow down't pack up acting so bleeding happy on jankers," said Private Calendar, my fellow prisoner, "so help me God I'll lob yow one up your crutch wit' sharp end of this bloody broom."

Calendar had come straight to the depot from Walton Jail and was suffering punishment for having hit the provost sergeant with the door torn from his locker. His outlook was understandably jaundiced. I recommended to him many of the precepts of Dale Carnegie and spent a lot of time during our penal periods together explaining that only by taking a positive approach to adversity can we lead the Full Life, Win Friends, and Influence People. I continued throughout the week to exemplify my points in my own behaviour, and it came as a sad disappointment when on the last day of my sentence he caught me bending over a bucket and lobbed me the threatened one up the crutch. To avoid getting him into further trouble I told the medical orderly that I had fallen astride when vaulting a five-barred gate.

"Looks to me," he said, as he painted everything in reach with gentian violet, "as if you was vaulting astride some biddy when she belted you one with her brolly."

I did my best to please Corporal Maloney, borrowing the *Weapon Training Manuals* from the depot library so that I could study beforehand each lesson in our training programme. I was thus able to prompt to corporal whenever he forgot any of his lines and to remind him of the correct Manual wording on the odd occasion when he made mistakes. Although he never directly thanked me—he was having trouble breaking in his new teeth at the time—I am sure he was grateful for these little services.

Our relations on drill parades were not as amicable as I would have wished. The root cause of dissension was my distinctive walk of the Goodbody family in which the same arm and leg swing forward together. The Army gait requires, unfortunately, the opposite routine. While a Goodbody swings left arm forward with left foot stepping out, the Army prefers that the right arm go forward as the left steps out.

By careful concentration and counting aloud I could meet the Army rhythm for the first few paces but then heredity would assert itself, the reflexes of my ancestors would regain control and my limbs slip steadily back to their natural unison, left going with left and right going with right. Another twenty yards and the counter-swinging arms of the men about me would begin to falter and join in half-heartedly with mine. By the time we'd been twice up and down the square the rhythmic uncertainty would spread throughout the squad and arms would be going all ways like insane sema- phores before the gibbering Maloney called a halt. At first he thought the Goodbody gait was a deliberate act of sabotage and hauled me out in front of the squad.

"So you're not satisfied, boyo, with smashing my dentures and visiting the pains of purgatory on my suffering gums. You want to put me in the ruddy loony-bin by playing Joe Cripple on drill parade, don't you?"

"No, Corporal. I always walk this way."

"Nobody walks that way. It's against human nature. . . . Quick march! . . . Halt! . . . About turn! . . . Quick march!"

He kept me jumping around with sudden orders for ten minutes in the hope that I would convict myself of mickey- taking by dropping into the Army rhythm. But, in the end, he had to concede my sincerity.

"What have I ever done," he asked, "that God Almighty should lumber me with you? You ought to be in a bloody circus, you did. Or hop-stepping up behind Groucho Marx. You're a horrible sight creeping around the square like a wooden-legged hunchback. Get off down behind the cook- house where nobody can see you and practise walking like a human being."

He came down to give me personal instruction, insisting that we walk together like a three-legged race. At the end of the session I hadn't made any notable progress, but Maloney was definitely picking up the Goodbody polka.

"You've got me doing it now, and I'm supposed to be the flaming drill instructor. Another six weeks of you and the whole depot'll have the cack-handed St. Vitus's Dance."

It was that evening that Calendar jabbed me so ungrate- fully with the broom handle. On parade next day I was forced to walk with legs held carefully apart, bandy as a cow- punching coot. This refinement of my normal style was just too much for Maloney.

"Jesus wept!" he groaned. "And all because he laid eyes on

[19]

you. Half man, half ruptured crab. And me on 7-4 in quid notes that our squad wins the Drill Competition. Take him away, Dodds. Get him excused drill and see if the orderly room can't use him till he can at least get his spavined hocks together again."

They sent me in to Sergeant Major Grope.

"I see from your records you claim to have been a chief clerk and accountant in civvy street. Does that mean you can read and write?"

"Yes, sir."

"Then you can start copying up the names on the acquittance rolls for next month. And don't think I won't be watching you ..."

They gave me last week's carbons, a foot high stack of pay sheets, and I set to work writing in the names of the twelve hundred-odd inhabitants of the depot. The last scribe had been in a hurry and some of his entries could have been more legible. The orderly room corporal showed me where I could check any doubtful names against the nominal rolls and personal records. It seemed an excellent opportunity to display to the sergeant major my powers of application, so I diligently cross-checked and struck balances at every possible point. My industry was rewarded when he came into the office after nine o'clock on my fourth evening and saw me still at work.

"Haven't you finished those sheets yet?" he said. "There shouldn't be any need to work till this time of night."

"I have completed the sheets, sir, and am now engaged in checking the accuracy of my entries. There are a number of discrepancies between the various records which I feel you should know about and I have, therefore, prepared a report for your consideration."

I handed him the top copy.

"As I have indicated, sir, at paragraph one, there are one thousand one hundred seventy-two other ranks on the present strength of the depot and one thousand one hundred eighty-four names on the pay sheets. One thousand one hundred eighty-four signatures appeared last week and therefore cash has been drawn and paid out in respect of twelve soldiers who are not on the strength. My analysis at paragraph two indicates that six of these extra names are those of recruits who have been discharged from the depot back to civilian status during the past year, three others are named J. Smith, two W. Robinson, and one E. Jones. While the appearance on the paysheets of the extra twelve names and the regular debiting of pay against their signatures may be due to some errors in the records I have examined so far, it may well suggest, as you will be aware, sir, that someone is engaged in embezzlement of Army funds. I was wondering, sir, who actually controls the drawing of cash and the balancing of the pay sheets."

"I do."

"Oh!"

"What I mean," said the sergeant major hastily, "is that I'm in *control* of the work, but there's all sorts of people have to help me. Officers write the cheques and give out the money, the clerks add up the pay sheets. Could be any of 'em." He sat down beside me and put a fatherly hand on my shoulder.

"Now, my boy, I think it would be best if we kept this entirely to ourselves. There may be some mistake in the records you don't know about. And anyway, if there is a villain about we don't want him to know we're on to him, do we?"

"No, sir. I have completed my duty in reporting to you."

"That's right. And you leave the rest to me." He tapped my report. "Have you by any chance got a copy of this?"

"Yes, sir. I thought I would keep one as a sample of my Army work. It might be useful if I get to any interviews."

He sucked his teeth judicially.

"I think it might be as well if you gave it to me. You can't be too careful about security."

I handed him the carbon.

[21]

"As you wish, sir. I'm sure I could remember the details if ever I should need them."

"You can, can you?" He looked at me keenly. "And about these interviews. Is there any particular line you'd like to get transferred to?"

"No, sir. I am anxious only to do my duty."

"I see. Well, you get off now. And remember, not a word to anybody about this."

"I'll remember, sir."

"And it'll perhaps be best if you don't work here no more. Just in case anybody's watching. Tomorrow morning, you report to the R. Q. M. S. for duty in the stores."

R. Q. M. S. Dibson was busy stock-taking and he set me to measuring flannelette, counting button sticks, pairing boots, and bundling blankets. In the process I was able to compare the Army stock records with those of Cawberry and Company and to suggest one or two improvements in his arrangements. He was not, unfortunately, very appreciative.

"Don't fink, son," he said. "Just count the fings I tell you to count and write down how many. That's all you got to do. Leave the brainwork to the Secretary of State for War, eh? All he pays you for is to do or die, not to reason why. Now get off with the truck party and help pick up the rations."

We had to wait a long time at the ration dumps and while the others played pontoon I had ample opportunity to study the system of issue. Corporal Maloney didn't seem anxious to have me back on normal duties and I was left for a most informative week in the stores. Despite R. Q. M. S. Dibson's strictures about thinking, I wrote out some observations for his consideration. It seemed only fair that he should have the same benefit of my experience as Sergeant Major Grope. I took my paper into his office during tea break.

"Excuse me, sir," I said, "but I have a short report on certain store-keeping points to submit for your consideration."

[22]

"I don't want no report. And you're on a charge for disobeying an order. I said no finking."

"The first point, sir, refers to our ration figures. While in the orderly room I established that there are one thousand one hundred seventy-two other ranks on the strength. Yet the figure on our indents used for meat, sugar, tinned fruit, bacon, and the other foodstuffs on the civilian ration list, is one thousand two hundred seventy-two. For these items we are thus receiving issues for one hundred people in error."

The R. Q. M. S. got up and bolted his office door.

"Go on," he said. "Tell me more."

"Fortunately, this error of one hundred is not repeated in the cookhouse figures. The actual rations issued to the cook sergeant are based on the correct strength of one thousand one hundred seventy-two. The one hundred surplus rations should therefore accumulate each day in your main store."

"Should they, indeed?"

"In theory, they should. And assuming the error has persisted for, say, one month, there should now be two Nissen huts full of surplus rations. In practice, however, except for the emergency forty-eight hour stock of corned beef and biscuits there is no accumulation whatever of civilian rationed foodstuffs anywhere in the store."

"Then where is it?"

"I don't know, sir. It would appear that the surplus one hundred rations are being removed daily elsewhere so that no accumulation arises."

"And do you know who's doing the removing?"

"No, sir. But I thought I should report the facts to you."

Dibson fanned himself with his hat.

"Phew! . . . But you have been a busy little bee, haven't you."

"I try to improve my knowledge all the time, sir."

"Very commendable. I'm sure." He sat me down and put his arm around my shoulder in just the way Sergeant Major

[23]

Grope had done. "Now you ain't told nobody about your figures, have you?"

"No, sir."

"Good. Then we'd better just keep this to ourselves until I can get my arrangements made for a proper investigation. If you should breathe one word of this to anybody else and jeopardize those investigations you'd be up for court-martial and in the glasshouse pronto. Understand?"

"Yes, sir."

"Good. I'll keep in touch with you. But I don't think it would be wise for you to work in my stores no more. You report up at the officers' mess tomorrow and tell the corporal I sent you to help him with his books."

"Yes, sir. And there's just one other point I think you ought to know. While I was dusting the gallon rum jars one of them fell over and the cork came out."

"Oh! Did any rum get spilt?"

"No, sir. The jar was full of cold tea. I thought you'd like to know."

He unbolted the door for me.

"You ain't after a transfer somewhere else are you, son? Wanting to better yourself maybe?"

"No, sir. Not at the moment, anyway."

At first the mess corporal was most grateful for my assistance, but his attitude towards me became strangely cooler on the third day when I showed him my poultry and egg analysis which proved that the bills from his supplier must have been wrongly made out. To have consumed all the poultry items charged for in the past quarter the twenty-two officers would have had to have eaten two chickens and eight eggs each per day. It was while I was explaining my figures to the corporal that a message came for me to dress up and report to the commanding officer.

"As you probably know, Goodbody," said the colonel, rubbing his white moustache and muttering behind the ac-

[24]

tive hand, "the country needs officers. One of my jobs is to find 'em. There's a draft of fifteen recruits selected from previous intakes due to go to 212 O. C. T. U. in two days' time. One of them has been careless and unpatriotic enough to get German measels. We've got to fill his vacancy on the course at short notice. Although you've only been with us barely a month you have been strongly recommended for the vacancy." He riffled through the papers on his desk. "Sergeant Major Grope and R. Q. M. S. Dibson both give you most exemplary recommendations for the earliest possible posting to O. C. T. U. and Corporal Maloney indicates that your abilities are such that you would not profit greatly by any longer period at his depot. The mess corporal also spoke to me at lunch in glowing terms about your work with him. . . . What about you? Do you think you could make an officer?

"I am prepared to do my best, sir, in any station to which my King and Country may see fit to call me."

"Are you a horseman?"

"Yes, sir." I had frequently ridden the puller of Cawberry and Company's delivery dray.

"Good show. I see you were a chief clerk and accountant. Who with?"

"Cawberry and Company, sir. . . . Corn-chandlers, sir."

"Know a bit about victualling horses, then, eh?"

We spent a jolly half hour discussing fodder in all its forms and the intricacies of the equine digestion. The colonel shook me by the hand at the end, wished me the best of luck at 212 O. C. T. U. and expressed his assurance that I would not let down the Old Depot.

As I packed my kit next day and drew my warrant I reflected how unfortunate had been my start in the Army and how unwise I would have been to have let it discourage me. If you persevere in the face of adversity and do your best at all times, your true worth will eventually be recognized by your

[25]

superiors. It was undoubtedly the hard work which I had done for Sergeant Major Grope and the R. Q. M. S. which had earned me such approbation. And if I had not tried to explain Dale Carnegie to Private Calendar I would never have got the chance to work in either the orderly room or the stores. Everything happens for the best in the end, of course, but I did not appreciate at the moment of Calendars impact that my first impetus towards becoming an officer and a gentleman had arrived in the form of a jab up the crutch with the sharp end of a broom.

Chapter Four

Generals have often been reproached with preparing for the last war instead of the next—an easy gibe when their fellow-countrymen and their political leaders, too frequently, have prepared for no war at all.

F.-M. SIR WILLIAM SLIM
Defeat Into Victory

Gort spoke much of the war in 1914–18 in which he was very well read. He criticized the handling of the British troops in 1914 at Le Cateau, on the Marne, and at the crossing of the Aisne. . . . On our way we crossed the Vimy Ridge. Gort got us out of our cars when we reached it. He made Hore-Belisha climb a very muddy bank and kept him shivering in the howling gale, while he explained the battle fought there in the 1914–18 war. . . . We stopped again, a few miles further on, to hear Pownall describe an attack on Auber's Ridge . . . twenty-odd years before . . .

MAJ. GEN. SIR JOHN KENNEDY
The Business of War

THE ACCENT AROUND ME changed from Enoch and Eli to best "cut glass." My new comrades seemed all aristocrats, juvenile stockbrokers, dons, undergraduates, and sons of tycoons. Plums grew in every throat and I took particular care to talk as far back in the mouth as possible and with every aspirate at my command.

"Welcome to 212 O. C. T. U.," barked Colonel Grapple, the C. O., baring his teeth and thrashing his leg with a riding whip. "Straight from the shoulder. That's m'way. Simple soldier-man. Cavalry fashion. All over the world.

[27]

M'job now to make officers. Make 'em or break 'em, by gad!"
Silk purses out of sow's ears. Some of you'll make silk purses.
Some'll never be anything but sow's ears. Get rid of them.
R. T. U.—Returned to Unit. Never mind. This is war.
Damned hard times. Got to be ruthless. Only way to beat the
Hun . . ."

I was most impressed by the staff of instructors. All were
seasoned warriors who had spent a lifetime in the Army.
Many were such valuable instructors that they could never be
spared for actual fighting and had devoted the whole of their
careers to lecturing about it.

Our days and nights were loaded with work and we learnt
how to inspect feet, salute when riding a bicycle, break step
on bridges, build a World War I trench system, and outwit
the wily Pathan. Major Hopfire, who wore spurs on his boots
and honey-coloured puttees, was the ultimate authority on all
things Pathan and advised us every Wednesday how hosilities
were conducted on the Northwest Frontier.

"Never underrate the Pathan," he would stress. "Damned
wily chap, Johnny Pathan. When you're under canvas always
keep the rifles chained to the tent pole. Otherwise, he'll have
'em. Strip himself mother-naked, greased all over and slippery as an eel, he'll slide under the brailings like a snake.
And if he can't get a rifle, he'll take the bolt. Wonderful
craftsmen, the Pathan. Make a barrel and stock as well as
anybody in Brummagem, but he can't make a bolt. You can't
temper steel on a cow-dung fire, can you? So always take the
bolt out, lock 'em in a box and chain that to the pole
too. . . . Any questions, so far?"

I had always made a point of asking at least one question at
every lecture. It showed the instructor that you were keen
and on the ball.

"Please, sir," I said, "have the Pathans gone over to Hitler?"

"No, they haven't. Too damned wily for that."

[28]

"Then shall we be fighting them in this war, sir?"

"Of course you will, lad. British Army's always been fighting the Pathans."

"What about, sir?"

"What about? . . . Well . . . about all sorts of things. Always trouble up on the Northwest Frontier. Army's job to fight, my boy, not keeping asking why, why, why all the blasted time."

"I'm sorry, sir. I just wondered why it was always the Pathans."

"Because, my lad, the Pathans are just like you are. Damned troublemakers. What's your name?"

He wrote my name in his little black book, muttering through his moustache that there were some right sow's ears in this latest lot. I had plainly slipped one rung down the R. T. U. ladder and I'm afraid that a later misunderstanding during Chemical Warfare brought further descent.

Sergeant Hoop, the Anti-Gas Instructor, suffered, unfortunately, from educational insecurity. He feared the superior intellects of the dons, barristers, and public school wanderers in his audience and was ever suspicious that they were trying to come it over him.

"What we are going on with now," he said from his platform, one drowsy afternoon, "is the use and handling of Anti-Gas Carpet. Now one roll of anti-gas carpet is proper to be held in each company stores. Anti-gas carpet is made of a number of laminated layers of heavy gauge paper specially coated with a chemical preparation which renders it resistant to liquid mustard gas. Anti-gas carpet is strong enough to support on normal ground the weight of troops in Full Service Marching Order. On encountering an area of liquid mustard gas advancing infantry should be given the command 'Halt!' and the anti-gas carpet should immediately be brought up. The standard roll of carpet is four feet six inches wide and twenty-five yards long. It should be laid on the ground six feet from the contaminated area and the securing tapes released. Two men should then be detailed to advance on the carpet unrolling it before them as they go. When the carpet has been laid completely across the contaminated area the remaining troops should proceed smartly across it. The anti-gas carpet is an expendable item of stores and should be left *in situ* and no attempt made to salvage any part of it. . . . Any questions?"

I stood up.

"Did you say, Sergeant, there was twenty-five yards in a roll?"

"That is correct."

"What do you do then, if having unrolled the anti-gas carpet and marched all your troops on to it, you find that the area of liquid mustard gas is fifty yards wide?"

Sergeant Hoop looked at me silently for a long time.

"What's your name?" he asked at last.

"Goodbody, Sergeant."

"Mr. Goodbody," he said precisely. "You want bull-f——ing."

He wrote my name in his little black book, too, and went straight on with "Decontamination of Motorcycles". I have never to this day had a proper answer to my question. And somewhere, troops could still be stranded in the middle of a fifty-yard gas patch on a twenty-five yard carpet.

In view of these failures to impress at Pathans and Chemical Warfare, it was fortunate for me that the War Office considered the most important subject in the training of an officer for World War II was the Design, Construction, and Furnishing of a Trench System for World War I. Half our waking hours were spent with pick and shovel excavating a second Ypres on Parsley Common. We built a labyrinth of trenches, six-feet across, sandbagged, loop-holed, revetted, fire-stepped, and duck-boarded throughout. Signposts with jocular names pointed the way through the warren, and we made vast dugouts equipped with bunks, candles in bottles, pinups on the walls, and all mod-con. Night after night we practiced trench reliefs, singing "Mademoiselle from Armentieres" and going over the top by numbers. I have always liked gardening and I really put my back into Trench Warfare. I was twice complimented verbally by Colonel Grapple himself; once on the smoothness of my spade backswing when digging in the crouch position, and again for the real spirit I put into the second chorus of "Tipperary."

The climax of our training, the final arbiter which sorted the field marshals from the R. T. U., was the series of Leadership Tests. We took turns at commanding our own sections on these exercises and were marked upon our control and initiative. It was a difficult task enforcing obedience from fellow cadets, and I had much trouble in dominating by personality Number 18 Section which included among its ten members one Lord, one Sir, an actor, two barristers, and a don. For men of their background and intellect I must say that they behaved at times with an immaturity which led me to doubt whether they would ever make responsible officers. I endeavoured to influence them by my own example of unfailing obedience when they were taking their turns of command. But my efforts made little impression on their irresponsibility and merely resulted in my time being wasted in carrying requisitions to Sergeant Hoop for twenty-six and a half yards of anti-gas carpet and decking myself in foliage as a mobile observation tree.

The exercise always started in Little Ypres, and when my turn came for command we went in one evening with the rest of A Company to do a trench relief of B Company, followed by a night approach march across six miles of Parsley Common to attack Nob Hill which would be held by C Company.

The night march was carried out by sections and after I had received my orders I lined up my troops in the support trench and briefed them in detail.

"And now," I said as I came to the end, "any questions?"

"Yes," said Lord George Huby. "When do we get our bleeding kip?" All the rest of the company got their heads down half an hour ago."

It was ten o'clock and we were due to move off at midnight.

"Before retiring," I said, "it will be useful if we just run through our notes on Night Patrols."

"You do, Cornbody," said Sir Rudolph Thrope, "and I run the toe of my boot up behind you."

I had noticed Major Hopfire coming out of the command dugout and pressed on.

"As you say, Cadet Thrope, when on night patrol the toe of the boot should always touch the ground first. Now why is this, Cadet Brechin?"

"Oblige me, mate," said Brechin, the actor, "by getting yourself quietly stuffed."

"Now then," said Major Hopfire as he came down the trench. "What's all this noise about?"

I stood up and saluted smartly, hitting the gas alarm gong with my elbow and bringing the company awake.

"No. 18 Section, sir. Cadet Goodbody in command. We are just revising our Night Patrol notes in preparation for the exercise."

"Then for Christ's sake stop it and let me get some blasted sleep. Always the same. Once a troublemaker, always a troublemaker."

He put another note in his little black book and went back to his cave. Which sent me off at midnight with neither a light heart nor a happy band of underlings.

It was black as pitch and drizzling steadily. We had four hours in which to reach the assembly point, Copse 483102. No. 18 Section was assigned as Fire Support Group and my nine men carried between them two Bren guns, two two-inch mortars, one antitank rifle and supplies of blank ammunition for all arms.

"They picked us for this," said Cromer, the barrister, as we waded uphill through the bracken, "because they couldn't find mules mug enough."

Going up against the skyline wasn't too bad, but I couldn't pick up a thing when we went down into the gulley beyond. I had to send Sir Rudolph out in front as guide-marker and take bearings on him every ten yards. At the bottom of the slope we ran into swamp. The guide-marker went in thigh-deep and we had to lifeline him out. We trekked north and we trekked south but everywhere before us spread the morass. When I tried to go back the way we'd come that, too, turned to peatbog. The night grew blacker and wetter and each boot was a club-footed hundredweight of mud. My nine subordinates floundered along under their loads and I could see at the end of an hour that their morale was getting low. It was my duty as commander to raise their spirits.

"Keep it up chaps," I cried. "Not much farther now. What about a jolly old sing-song? Let's have a rousing go at 'Ten Green Bottles'!"

"If anybody sings a blasted note," said Lord George Huby, "I'll beat his bloody brains out with these mortar bombs."

I struck up the song myself and I'm sure that my own cheerfulness would have spread to the others if, just when I was down to four green bottles hanging on the wall, Lord George had not slung a case of mortar bombs overarm and hit me square in the small of my back. I slithered forward under the force of the blow and, as I sat down in the mud, the compass shot from my hands and fell into an outcrop of reeds.

I prised myself out of the glue. This was my testing time. Now was the moment to exert my powers of command. If I let this indiscipline pass the whole section might become a disorderly rabble.

"Number 18 Section," I commanded. "Halt! Cadet Huby, did you throw those bombs at me?" His lordship was sitting on a rock in the rain.

"I'm bloody stacking," he said. "Two hours wading knee-deep behind you and we're not half a mile on our way."

"Cadet Huby," I ordered sharply. "Pick up your mortar bombs and fall in."

"Sam! Sam!" said Brechin. "Pick up tha musket."

"I've fallen in, mate," said Lord George. "Three times already. Up to my perishing waist."

"Are you refusing to obey an order of your section commander?" I asked calmly.

"I'm fed up with you as section commander, Corny-boy. All you're after is getting us drowned."

"This is mutiny," I said.

"By God! Mr. Christian," intoned Brechin. "This is mutiny. I'll see you hang from the highest yardarm on Plymouth Hoe!"

"Cadet Huby," I said. "You are under arrest for mutiny in that you have refused to obey a lawful order of your section commander."

Cromer the barrister came out of the darkness.

"Under arrest, eh? What sort of arrest?"

"Close arrest."

"Close arrest? Then he'll need an escort. Laid down in *King's Regulations* that an officer under close arrest must be escorted at all times by an officer of equivalent rank."

"All right then. You're his escort."

Nobody was going to out-face me on military law. Cromer put down his Bren and unslung his clutch of magazines.

"Then I can't carry these. The first duty of an escort is to secure his prisoner. If Huby runs away I'll never catch him carrying that lot. And *K.Rs.* state plainly that prisoners under close arrest must be disarmed. So he can't carry that two-inch mortar. He might turn it on me."

"I am well aware, Cadet Cromer," I said, "of the requirements of *King's Regulations*. . . . Cadet Brechin, you will take over Cadet Lord Huby's mortar and bombs."

[34]

"What me? I'm carrying a mortar and a load of bombs already. And half a ton of magazines. It's handsome they call me, cully, not Samson."

"I am ordering you, Cadet Brechin, to take up that mortar."

He dropped his load in the mud and held out his wrists.

"Put the cuffs on me, Corporal. I'm under close arrest, too, I'm joining the Lord George Huby mutiny."

"And I'll volunteer to escort him," said Sir Rudolph, dropping his antitank rifle on the dump. "Dangerous bastard he may be, but I'll handle him."

He pulled Brechin's arm up behind him in a policeman's lock. The other five clustered about me, obviously hopeful that I would order them to add to their loads and thus give them opportunity to become prisoner or escort and lay down their present burdens. Fortunately, I kept my head and circumvented them all.

"We will proceed on to the objective," I ordered. "Cadets Huby and Brechin under close arrest and escorted by Cadets Cromer and Thrope respectively. I will carry their loads."

By carefully distributing mortars, bombs, and magazines about all hangable points of my person, taking a Bren gun over one shoulder and an antitank rifle over the other I managed to get all the dump off the ground. Then I remembered the compass and had to divest myself again to search among the reeds. When I found it, it was full of mud.

"Never mind," I said indomitably, "we will march by the stars."

"Bethlehem," said Brechin, "here we come."

The pole star found us, at last, a way through the swamp and we toiled on across rolling eternities of wet bracken. Burdened as I was with firearms, half drowning in a river of sweat, I could not give proper attention to astronomy and at 04.00 hours, when we should have been assembling at Copse 483102, we came up to the gates of a farmyard.

[35]

"We're right off the talc, Commander," said Sir Rudolph, bending with me over the pulping map. "There's no farmhouse within ten miles of the copse."

"If they'd lend us a room," said Cromer eagerly, "we could have a drumhead court-martial."

"Section may stand easy," I ordered. "I will inquire our present position at the farm and plot a new course."

Too weary to untwine my trappings I stumbled across the yard looking for the front door. As I came round the corner of the cowsheds the lights of a car blazed suddenly out and four men with shotguns came from the shadows.

"Get him, Tiger! Take him, Rex!"

Two shark-headed wolf dogs bounded on me, one fastening his jaws round my left gaiter, the other mounting his front paws on my chest and bearing me back against the byre. The Bren, the antitank rifle and one mortar fell away from me.

"Robbed an armoury already, he has, boss," said one of the four, "and he's got British uniform on."

"Keep him covered, boys. They reckon there was more than one parachute seen coming down."

A fat man in riding breeches came through the lights and waved a pistol at me.

"*Sprechen Sie Deutsche?*" he shouted.

"No," I said. "For God's sake call these dogs off."

"*Heil Hitler! Wo ist dein parachuten?*"

"I'm British. I'm an officer cadet. Here's two of my section now."

Brechin and Lord Huby came across the yard.

"*Ach! Mein Gott!*" said Brechin. "*Die Hunden haben unser Kapitan gebitten.*"

"Germans, by God!" yelled the fat man. "Keep 'em covered, boys."

"*Donner and Blitzen!*" said Huby. "*Die englisch Schwein* have nobbled uns. *Wir mussen essen die* secret code."

"Don't fool about," I said, "speak English."

[36]

"*Ach!* But yes," said Brechin. "We are good British Tommy Atkins, what ho. Many Happy Returns of the Day."

"Turkish wolfhounds, those are," said Huby. "Trained to guard harems and go straight for the genitals. One false move, Kapitan, and *du bist ein eunuch.*"

"Hold him, Tiger," said the farmer. "Get over against the wall with him, you two. . . . Run over and get the general, Danny. Tell him we captured them parachutists."

"*Kamerad!*" pleaded Brechin. "*Kamerad!* We surrender, *Herr Englander.*"

With dogs at my gaiters and guns at our heads they kept us pinned there for ten minutes until a shooting brake screeched into the yard. A figure in a British warm and braided cap jumped out.

"Where are they?" he barked, his white moustache glittering. "Where are the damned Huns?"

"Good Lord!" said Huby. "Uncle General Athelstan."

"Bless my boots!" puffed the general. "Young Huby. With your face blacked up like a damned music hall. What the hell's going on here?"

Blood relationship was reluctantly accepted as *bona fides* by Athelstan's Private Army and the dogs were called off my gaiters. Lord Huby explained the situation.

". . . and we're supposed at this moment to be giving fire support while the rest of the company assault Nob Hill."

"Nob Hill, boy! You're eight miles off course."

"Then we'll all be R.T.U.'d for this shambles. Cornbody'll probably be sent to the glasshouse."

"Never give up, my boy. See what we can do. Get in the brake and I'll take you to Nob Hill anyway."

We woke up the rest of the section who were sleeping in a hayloft and piled into and over the brake. It sagged heavily on the bends but the general heaved it through the lanes towards the dawn breaking behind Nob Hill. Retired Indian Army, Huby said he was, rising seventy-five, D.S.O. and bar, curry in his blood and fire in his breath. He bullied the brake off the road and up a forest track, finally stopping in a clearing.

"Nob Hill is just over the top," he said, "you lie low while I make a recce."

He came back in ten minutes.

"Had a crack with young Bertie Hopfire," he said. "Your company went in without fire support. Hopeless failure. All captured and up there disarmed with faces like fiddles."

"There's nothing to be done then," I said, "but to go up and explain to the major."

"Explain? . . . Explain nothing, my boy. No damned spirit these days, that's the trouble. Attack! That's the only thing. Nothing to lose. Everything to gain. You've not been captured. No umpire has said you're wiped out. So get in amongst 'em. Counterattack!"

"But there's only ten of us, sir. There's about a hundred and twenty of them up there."

"Then you'll have to cut them down to size. You could take them on if they were disarmed, couldn't you?"

"Yes . . . but how do we disarm them?"

"The way the Pathans do it."

"You mean strip mother-naked sir, and grease ourselves all over?"

"I'll be back on mutiny," said Brechin. "I'm not dragging no bare belly through that bracken."

"No time for exhibitionism," said the general. "Now what, in every exercise, is always served on the objective?"

"A hot meal," I said. "Hot meal will be served on the objective."

"Correct. And that's what's happening now. They're feeding and Hopfire has made them pile arms, Brens and all, very neatly for our purpose. There's two sentries on the arms but I'll keep them distracted for a minute while you get cracking.

[38]

There's a load of climbing rope in the brake, six of you get that and come up with me. Two of you get up a tree with the Brens. The other two get the mortars ranged. . . . When you hear the whistle all four blaze away with blanks, smoke, star shells, and anything else they've allowed you . . ."

As we stalked alongside, the brake moved quietly up to the top of the hill. The general stopped behind a screen of bushes.

"Twenty yards through there is where they've piled arms. Work all together when I get the sentries turned away."

It was the only time in the whole war that I saw anybody pile arms. Somewhere about, I felt, must be Gunga Din. There they were stacked, a hundred and twenty rifles, butts to the ground in groups of eight, muzzles together in neat pyramids, held in place by linked swivels. It was a sight to gladden the heart of any wily Pathan.

As the general gripped the sentries in conversation we slid out as one man, threaded a length of rope through the slings of two or three pyramids each, looped up six recumbent Brens and were back beneath the bracken again and hidden from view. Cromer got into the brake while we mounted through the back doors, hitching the rope ends round the bumper.

I blew my whistle. The brake revved up and shot away, the hundred and twenty rifles vanished from the clearing, clattering along through the bracken and down the track. The Bren men in the tree opened up, star shells burst in the sky, smoke bombs fell fifty yards away and the dawn wind scudded the grey clouds over the feeding C Company. . . . We let go the rope ends, the rifles dropped off, Cromer swung hard about and yelling madly, cracking blanks, and blowing whistles, we roared like an armoured car into the middle of the camp.

For full five glorious minutes we drove up and down, round and round, scattering men and mess tins in a turmoil

[39]

of mud and smoke and glimmering flares. Then the ammunition ran out, vision cleared, the noise died away and we stopped before the figure of Major Hopfire waving gallantly in our path.

I leapt out and saluted smartly.

"Number 18 Section all present and correct, sir. We lost our way, arrived late at the objective and have made our counterattack."

"The rifles, man!" he yelled. "What have you done with C Company's rifles? They're all on my damned charge."

I saluted again.

"We captured them, sir. We remembered your lectures and made like the wily Pathan."

Suddenly, all the fury went out of him. I believe he really loved his lifelong enemy, the Pathan.

"Really, my boy. You did all this, with just one section? All this? . . ." He gestured around at the moaning, mud-spattered cadets, the overturned dixies, the congealing stew. "And you captured one hundred and twenty rifles by marking my words and making like the Pathan. Dear old Johnny Pathan. . . ."

I turned away to avoid embarrassing my superior officer by watching his emotion. The general slipped into his brake and drove quietly away. A giant cadet from C Company came towards me with a frying pan rampant.

"You leave him alone," said Lord George Huby aristocratically, "or I'll tear your bloody ears off."

Sir Rudolph Thrope, Brechin, and Cromer gathered to disarm my attacker and roll him in the mud. I felt proud that my example during the long night and my leadership of the attack had so clearly won their loyalty. I could afford to be magnanimous in victory.

"In view of your devotion to duty during the counterattack on Nob Hill, I have decided to release you both from close arrest, Cadets Huby and Brechin, and to withdraw the charge against you of mutiny. I trust, however, that you will not construe this leniency as in any way condoning your previous conduct nor indicating—"

And it was then, to my further disappointment, that Lord George Huby hit me with the C Company frying pan.

Chapter Five

Hitler . . . issued the directive for the invasion of England—Operation Sea Lion. . . .
. . . The landing operation must be a surprise crossing on a broad front extending approximately from Ramsgate to a point west of the Isle of Wight. . . . For the Army operations forty divisions will be required . . . about a hundred thousand men with appropriate equipment including heavy gear must be transported in the first wave. . . .

ANTHONY MARTIENNSEN
Hitler and his Admirals

We had hardly any anti-tank guns or ammunition and very little field artillery in the country . . . when Mr. Churchill visited the beaches of St. Margaret's Bay, near Dover, the officer in charge of the anti-invasion defences explained rather apologetically that he had only three anti-tank guns in the whole brigade, which covered five miles of this coast nearest France, with six rounds for each gun. He wondered whether he was justified in firing one of these rounds to show the men how the gun worked. . . .

GEN. SIR LESLIE HOLLIS
War at The Top

THE FIGHTERS WERE MAKING silver plume patterns in the sky as I came out of Fenton Maltravers station on a July afternoon in 1940, one bright pip shining on each shoulder, newly commissioned in the Fourth Musketeers. I was alone in the sunshine on the gravel forecourt, empty and peaceful as Adlestrop. The porter came out of his cubbyhole and scattered corn to a single white hen.

"I say, my man," I called to him in my officer's voice. "Has transport been sent for me from the Fourth Musketeers?"

[42]

He paused with a fistful of grain.

"You talking to me?"

"Yes."

"Well, I bain't your man. And a truck come an hour ago but your train was late so it went away."

"Can I get a taxi?"

"No. He be gone over to Dorchester. Won't be back 'fore tea time."

"How far is it to the headquarters of the Fourth Musketeers?"

He considered for a moment as the hen pecked at his boot-laces.

"Not far. Straight down the road. Fair mile or thereabouts."

"Thank you, my man."

It was my duty to report to my commanding officer at the earliest possible moment. I picked up my valise and suitcase and set off down the lane. The tar was bubbling like seaweed in the afternoon heat. I was wearing my greatcoat and service cap and after half an hour's march sweat was trickling down my legs and dripping off the end of my nose.

The porter had badly underestimated the distance to Spelborough Park, the stately home on the Dorset coast at which the Fourth Musketeers had encamped after their return from Dunkirk. It was well over three miles and I made all speed I could, finally tottering into the adjutant's office with my tongue dust-dried and my legs newly off a Turkish bath treadmill.

I put down my luggage gratefully and saluted as smartly as my numbed arm could move.

"Second Lieutenant Goodbody reporting for duty, sir."

All I could see of Captain Tablet above his piled in-trays was the glossy black top of his head as he bent busily over his papers. He gave no sign that he had seen or heard me and went on with his writing. I stood to attention before his desk for full three minutes and the silence was broken only by the

[43]

squeak of his pen as it turned the corners. A chair stood invitingly near. My knees were trembling with fatigue.

"Excuse me, sir," I said. "Do you mind if I sit down?"

He put down his pen and blotted the last line. Then he looked up at me, eyebrows arched in surprise, umbrage shrinking his pale pomeranian face.

"Sit down?" he said, horrified as Squeers. "I haven't told you you can stand at ease yet."

He went back to his work and kept me wavering there for another five minutes. At the end of which time he signed me on the strength and allocated me to C Company and Major Arkdust. I was naturally disappointed at Captain Tablet's reception but recalled that the Fourth was a regular battalion. His attitude could therefore be due to that subconscious feeling of inferiority which beset many regular officers in the early days of the war when confronted with an influx of educated, wordly-wise civilians, and which expressed itself consciously in the form of barking and antipathy. So I mentally forgave him and followed my guide to C Company.

Major Arkdust's ginger hair was going back at the front but what he lost on the temples he made up on the moustache. Even at peace his eyeballs threatened apoplexy.

"I'm giving you Twelve Platoon and I want to see you pull 'em into shape." He leaned forward in his chair and poked my stomach with his swagger stick. "And yourself, too. You're carrying too much round the middle. If the Boche ever capture you, you'll be a cert for the soap boiler."

He rose from his chair to shame me, two gaunt yards and more of him, and took me to the stables and Number Twelve Platoon.

I will never forget that moment when I took over my first command. I can still catch the impermeable smell of the stables and see my faithful forty ranked before me on the cobbles.

"Stand easy, chaps," I said. "I'd just like to say a few words."

[44]

I wanted from the outset to win their confidence and let them feel that even though I was an officer I could understand the feelings of ordinary chaps like them.

"I want you to know right away," I said, "how pleased I was when Major Arkdust told me I was to be your platoon commander. I just know we're going to get on splendidly together. If you play ball with me, I'll play ball with you. You do your bit and I'll do mine. We're all members of the same team, each playing his part in the fight for Freedom and Democracy. Together let us work hard, train hard, and play hard. If the Boche should land on our shores, let us show him that good old Twelve Platoon is fit and ready to hit him for six back into the sea. I want you to look upon me not only as your platoon commander but also as a friend. If any of you have any problems on your minds do not hesitate to come and see me about them. I want you to feel you can come to me for help as you would to your own father . . ."

"Hullo, Dad," said a back-rank voice. "Mum's been looking all over for you."

"What about them that had no fathers?" muttered Private Drogue. "What about us bastards?"

"Shut up!" snapped Sergeant Transom.

That evening five of my soldiers came for personal interviews. Four of them were after an advance of pay, just trying me out for financial stupidity. The fifth, Private Clapper, rotund and balding like a monk, thundered briskly across the boards of the tack room.

"I been hearings things, sir," he said, "about her. I got mates still up at the brickworks and there's my mum writes to me every other day. Not that she'd say nothing in as many words against my missus, but I can read between the lines if you know what I mean. It's that insurance man, sir. He keeps after her. Comes round every Monday regular as clockwork for one-and-a-tanner a week on the funeral policy and gets his hoggins at the same time."

"His hoggins?"

[45]

"Yes, sir. Writes down the eighteen-pence in the book with his indelible pencil, whips off his shoes and over goes my missus."

"You mean he has . . . ahem . . . he has intercourse with your wife?"

"Yes, sir. And me still paying hire-purchase on the sofa. Every Monday afternoon he's at her and it's getting on my nerves. I can't eat no dinner of a Monday for thinking about it. Is it right, sir, when a soldier's away fighting for his King and Country that insurance men should keep coming round and having their hoggins off his wife?"

"No," I said. "Decidedly not."

"Thank you, sir."

"And what action, Clapper, were you proposing to take in the matter?"

He drew stiffly to attention and looked fixedly over my head.

"I will do just whatever you advise me, sir."

"Oh! . . . Yes . . . I see."

I must confess to having been a little taken aback by his faith in my wisdom. Obviously my homily had been more inspiring than I had expected. Although I did know a little about insurance, I was not at all well informed about female marital infidelity.

"Do you gather," I asked, "that your wife is a willing partner in this . . . er . . . in this hoggins business?"

He rolled his eyes to heaven in pious horror.

"Never, sir. Never in all her sweet days. It's him, sir. Suave, he is, sir. Homburg hat, suède shoes, umbrella and all that. Turned her head, he has, with all his la-di-da talk. Pulls the educated madam over the poor kid and she don't know whether she's coming or going."

I ran through my O.C.T.U. notebooks but they'd told us nothing at good old 212 about the appropriate tactic for Clapper's trouble. I considered the problem for some minutes while he patiently awaited a miracle. Then inspiration came.

"I know, Clapper," I said. "We'll lapse the policy!"

"Lapse the policy, sir."

"Yes. Then the insurance man won't call every Monday any more."

He gave a little jump of admiration.

"That'll have him, sir. Why didn't I think of that? Lapse the policy and then he'll have to go somewhere else for his hoggins."

"I'll draft you a letter to the insurance company."

"Thank you very much, sir."

He hammered down a right turn and rumbled out. I felt very satisfied. I had solved my first welfare problem. Word of my sagacity would no doubt get around the men.

Three days later C Company was sent down to the beaches and Twelve Platoon was allocated two miles of the Dorset coast to defend.

"And above all things," said Major Arkdust at the end of his order group, "conserve your ammunition. All we've got is fifty rounds per man and a thousand box per platoon in reserve. When you've used it all up, fix bayonets and charge."

I took Sergeant Transom out on reconnaissance.

"We'd better have our main position up here, sir," he said, prodding the cliff top with a bayonet.

"We'll get a better field of fire along the beach, Sergeant, if we go down to the undercliff."

He argued a bit but finally gave in when I quoted to him from Colonel Grapple's lectures on Trench Warfare.

My experience on Parsley Common suggested that it would take a fortnight to build a habitable emplacement. I was amazed when the platoon sergeant reported next day that the job was done; and utterly horrified to find on inspection that all he had dug was a series of narrow trenches about three feet wide.

[47]

"Really!" I said. "These rabbit scrapes will never do. Where's the berm? The parados? The counterscarp? The fire step? And what about the duckboards and the dugouts?"

"We don't want no dugouts. Slit trenches, that's all we want. Like we had in France. Narrower they are, the better they keep the shrapnel out."

A good soldier, no doubt, was Sergeant Transom in Peshawar, Palestine, and Dunkirk, but he lacked, of course, my advantage of up-to-the-minute O.C.T.U. training. I showed him the drawings of Army regulation trenches in my notebook and he freely admitted that he had never seen anything like them in all his born days. As was to be expected, his platoon was equally ill-informed. It took me twenty minutes of strenuous man-management to convince them that I was serious about wanting the trenches extended to six feet six inches wide. Private Drogue said he thought maybe I'd come from E.N.S.A. to give them a bit of a giggle. Finally, discipline triumphed and they set to work with all the jocularity of a chain gang to build War Office standard fortifications.

As I left them and walked back up to the cliff top, I noticed a civilian, middle-aged and male, watching suspiciously from the road.

"Excuse me," he said, "but I see you're digging your trenches in the undercliff."

We had been warned to look out for spies. I studied his cheeks carefully. Up near the left eye was a mark that could have been a sabre scar.

"*Heil Hitler!*" I snapped, remembering the Parsley Common farmer. One flicker of automatic response and I was poised ready to slit the lining out of his mackintosh.

"Eh?"

"*Heil Hitler, dummkopf!*"

"Excuse *me*," he said and scurried off down the road.

My finished battlements were superb. Not for nothing had I been runner-up for the 212 Spade of Honour. Dorset was safe for democracy behind a serrated crescent of Passchendaele earthworks. Six feet six across, seven feet deep, every wall was revetted with garden fencing and duckboards made from beer crates paved every inch of the way. The parapet was five feet thick, loop-holed cunningly for snipers, and there were covered shelter trenches at the rear, underground latrines, subterranean cook houses and dugouts of all sizes furnished like the palaces of troglodyte kings. Once he had realized that I was not to be diverted from my purpose, Sergeant Transom had kept the troops hard at it and they'd finished the work in eight days.

Proudly, I took Major Arkdust on a tour of inspection. He said not a word as we walked around the fortifications but I could see by the progressive popping of his eyeballs and the red twitching of his moustache that he was deeply impressed. He finally spoke when I took him into my headquarters dugout. It had double bunks on each side and for full effect I had lit a candle in a bottle and fixed saucy pinups on the walls.

"Great God Almighty in Heaven Above!" he said. "What are you going to do in there? Play *Journey's End?*"

I laughed obediently.

"Where did you work in civvy street, Goodbody? At the Imperial War Museum?"

"No, sir. I was with Cawberry and Company . . . the corn-chandlers."

"Then what the hell made you build this 1914 catacomb?"

"The trenches are dug strictly to War Office specifications, sir. As you will see." I handed him Volume III of my note books, open at 'Trench Design and Construction.'

He riffled through the pages, the ends of his moustache coming erectile with scorn.

"By God!" he said. "And did they teach you how to port arms with bows and arrows?"

"No, sir."

He weighed the volume in his hand.

[49]

"That lot won't help you to kill any Germans, will it? Not unless you hit them with it." And with a boomerang action, he threw my notebook into the sea. As my civilian's guide to trench warfare floated out on the ebb tide, gulls fought over it like a square, black mackerel.

"Fill 'em in, my lad. At once." He marked his measurements on the turf. "Slit trenches, that's what I want, not bloody dry docks. Or elephant traps. Fill 'em in to no more than three feet wide. And I'll be back in forty-eight hours to see them."

I was now in a delicate military position. I had lost my notes on Trench Warfare and as my forty soldiers came before me on parade they showed obvious symptoms of spade-weariness.

"Well, chaps." I said, smiling brightly to instill confidence, "Major Arkdust is very pleased with our work. Very pleased, indeed. Except for just one small point of detail . . . he thinks they're just a bit too wide."

"How much too wide?" asked Sergeant Transom grimly.

"Not all that much, really . . ."

"About three feet six inches too big, maybe?"

"As a matter of fact," I said, "yes. He just wants slit trenches three feet wide."

"Like we had before?"

"Yes. I'm afraid so. Like we had before."

My whole command went up in wailing and lamentation. They held out their hands to me exhibiting their blisters like Bombay beggers seeking backsheesh.

"Dig some slit trenches, he says," moaned Private Drogue.

"Then open 'em like Bechers bleeding Brook, he says. Now make 'em small again, he says. We couldn't be worse off if the Jerries took over." His colleagues questioned my sanity directly, my birth obliquely, and were unanimous that they'd be sexually abused before they'd put wounded hand to shovel again. It seemed to me an excellent opportunity for Sergeant Transom to practice his powers of control, so I asked him to

[50]

carry on. By the time I regained the road he had them filling in and their curses rumbled up the cliff like mutiny day at Sing Sing. That civilian was up there on the watch again.

"Hello," he said. "Filling them in again now, are you? If I'd been you, I'd never have dug them there in the first place."

"Fortunately," I said, "you are not me. When I need your advice on the selection of fields of fire, I'll ask for it, thank you."

"I was only trying to help . . ."

"And, furthermore, I would remind you that you are in a beach defence area and liable to arrest under security regulations . . ." I clapped my hand to my revolver and he ran off down the road and into a house. I made a mental note of the address.

The platoon finished their desecreation in good time and Major Arkdust pronounced his satisfaction with the slit trenches. To me, those utility earthworks just had no style at all. After the baroque magnificence of my bastions, it was a workhouse way of making war. I hoped devoutly that the Boche would not attack our portion of Dorset. I'd have been utterly ashamed to be caught by professional Junkers in such ridiculous rabbit scrapes.

"Thank you, chaps, for working so hard," I said on parade. "The company commander is again very pleased. But there's just one detail I would like to stress."

"So help me God!" muttered Private Drogue. "If he wants 'em opening out again, I'm going straight over to Hitler."

"I'd like to stress," I went on, "that you should never on any account prick blisters. The correct treatment is to . . ." Which gave me a lead-in to a most useful and much appreciated lecture on First Aid in the Field.

It rained interminably during the next fortnight. A spring burst up on the path down to the undercliff. The blue mud was so slippery that we had to fit ropeways to lower ourselves down. As I slithered along one pouring evening the voices of

[51]

my men came grumbling back like a Russian rising. Battle-ship *Potemkin* might have been anchored below.

"I can't get my flipping feet in, Sarge, never mind no Bren."

"Come out of there, Clapper, and get back here," shouted Sergeant Transom, "before you get yourself man-trapped."

My trenches in the undercliff had shrunk. Their meagre three-feet width had dwindled to six inches. The saturated clay had begun to flow like lava down the cliff face and was slowly, inexorably, filling in our foxholes.

I ordered a strategic withdrawl to the top of the cliff. Our scrambling accelerated the slide and we stood in the misty rain and watched in fascination as the lips of our trenches moved finally together. In ten minutes they were as closely sealed as Baldwin's, the slope of clay was smooth as silk and there was no sign to show that Twelve Platoon had ever struck spade.

Sergeant Transom sighed wearily.

"Dig 'em up here now, sir?" he asked indicating the same turf he had spitted with his bayonet five weeks before.

"Yes," I said, looking away from him and out to sea.

"Slit trenches, sir?"

"Yes."

"Three feet wide, sir?"

"Yes."

Private Drogue knelt in the wet and beat his head on the ground.

"Dig 'em small, dig 'em big, dig 'em small again. . . . Now close your eyes and I'll make 'em disappear. I tell you he ain't a British officer at all. He's a fifth columnist sent by Hitler to soften up Dorset."

"They dropped him by parachute, mate, dressed as a ruddy nun."

"Jonah, that's what he is. Bad luck Jonah. And please Gawd send Twelve Platoon a bloody great whale."

It seemed another excellent opportunity for Sergeant Transom to show whether he was officer material, so I left him to carry on. That civilian spy was waiting for me up on the road once more. This time, I decided, I would have to arrest him.

"Evening," he said. "Going to dig them up on top now, eh?"

"Yes. Now I warned you last time . . ."

"You should've dug them up there in the first place. Hopeless on the undercliff. Blue slipper clay, those cliffs are. Runs like pudden in the rain. I could have told you when you first started that they'd only close up in the autumn."

"Then why didn't you?"

"You wouldn't let me."

I was about to change the charge and arrest him for withholding information likely to be of assistance to the military authorities when I noticed Private Drogue picking up his rifle and pointing it our way. I had not yet had opportunity to check whether he was fully trained in the use of the safety catch, and deemed it wiser to leave the matter till another day and beat it for dead ground.

Chapter Six

From him I learned the value of really imaginative training. . . . Exercises organized by Wavell were always a challenge and a joy, never a bore. There was one, for instance, in which our 5th Brigade was sent to protect the Golden Fleece—of all things!

LT. GEN. SIR BRIAN HORROCKS
A Full Life

The 6th Brigade were custodians of the Fleece—a genuine sheepskin dyed yellow—which was hidden on the Surrey-Sussex border. The Argonauts were represented by 4th and 5th Brigades. . . . Wavell had given strict orders that every man in the Division must have the legend of the Golden Fleece explained to him so that he could take a real interest in what was going on.

BRIG. BERNARD FERGUSSON
Wavell: Portrait of a Soldier

THROUGH THE DARK DAYS of 1940 we stood with our backs to the wall, manning the beaches and ever ready to hurl back the Hun from the green hills of Dorset. Then as the peril passed and production flowed, military minds turned to thoughts of the offensive. Our division was withdrawn to strategic reserve and set upon a series of exercises infinitely more arduous and fatiguing than actual war. Umpires possessed of inexhaustible reserves and ingenious cruelty lurked at every cross road, food was but rarely allowed to break through and sleeping at all, even though it be blanketless in the snow, was a mark of dishonour.

The divisional commander, Major General Trugg, was

fond of recalling the privations of his own Army youth and assuring us that the exercises he was now setting were but garden parties compared with the maneuvers of total peace. As was his custom before each exercise, he gathered all his officers together in a cinema one morning in the autumn of 1941.

"We're going to have an exercise," he chirped from the stage, silhouetted before a giant diagram. "A real exercise, too. One of the good old good ones. Finest and toughest exercise ever held between the wars. Conducted by General Wavell when he had Second Division. Exercise 'Golden Fleece.' Something that'll really catch the imagination of the men. The legend of Jason and the Golden Fleece. We'll have a proper fleece dyed yellow and it'll be hidden in Hurt Wood on the Surrey–Sussex border and the Argonauts'll have a week's fighting before they get there . . ."

And with imperious pointer and timed intervals for coughing, he conducted us on his monster chart through the basic steps of our company purgatory.

A week later, after marching for two days and a night back and forth across the North Downs, the Fourth Musketeers dug in on the Surrey–Sussex border. C Company was in reserve, earmarked for the attack next morning as the first wave of the Argonauts. Major Arkdust was finishing his order group when a dispatch rider swung into the farmyard.

"Special message, sir," he said. "For immediate action."

Captain Croker, second in command, opened it.

"Addendum No. 8" he read aloud, "to Exercise Instruction No. 44. The Divisional Commander has given strict orders that every man in the division must have the legend of Jason and the Golden Fleece explained to him, so that he can take a real interest in what is going on. Umpires will be questioning individuals about the legend and company commanders will render personal certificates by o6.oo hrs. that the story of Jason has been explained to all ranks."

[55]

"The first thing to ask ourselves," said Major Arkdust, the clearest-minded man I ever served under, "is Jason who?"

I was educated on the science side myself and not well up on mythology. My fellow officers were regulars, simple soldiermen, as Captain Croker observed, who left books and all that sort of thing to the memsahibs. Grand lot of chaps to have beside you in a tight corner, mark you, but nobody knew the story of the Golden Fleece.

"You're responsible for company intelligence, Goodbody," said Major Arkdust. "So get yourself some intelligence about this Jason johnny and pass it on to the men."

I took my literary quest to the nearest village. A lady wearing a cloth cap and smoking a clay pipe opened the first cottage door.

"Good evening, madam," I said. "Would you by any chance have a copy of the legend of the Golden Fleece in the house?"

"Not today, thank you." She spat accurately on the hearthstoned step and closed the door.

The next three households thought I was a billeting officer and refused to open up. The door of "Zeebrugge" was opened by a retired admiral who demanded what the living hell I thought I was doing knocking people up about blasted fairy stories.

"Damned pongoes!" he snorted. "Jackassing about the country side. You'll lose the blasted war yet, that's what you'll do. . . . What's your name? I'll write to *The Times* about you."

I said my name was Dai Rees and my regiment, the Welsh Guards. The grocer wondered that a grown man like me hadn't something better to do with my time. The first straight answer I got was from the postmaster who set the dog on me. Eventually the village schoolmaster took pity on my youth and found me a copy of the *Child's Wonder Book of Greek Mythology*.

[56]

"It's meant for eight-year-olds," he said, "so it should be just right for arrested adolescents who play your sort of military games."

It was near lights-out when I got back to the battlefield and had the company assembled in a barn.

"What we're going on with now," I said, "is the legend of Jason and the Golden Fleece. The general wants you to remember the details during the exercise so that you can take a real interest in what is going on. So please feel free to ask questions."

"Blind O'Reilly," said Private Spool. "Bedtime stories."

"Once upon a time," I read from the book, "there was a Greek hero named Jason who sailed to Colchis to find the Golden Fleece. The Fleece came from the ram which swam from Thebes to the Black Sea with the boy Phrixus on its back . . ."

Private Parkin, wireless operator from H. Q. Company, overeducated, son of an M. P., barrack room K. C., stood up.

"Thebes to the Black Sea, sir? Four hundred miles or more? A ram, swimming, with a boy on his back?"

"Rams can't swim," said Private Drogue. "They cut their throats with their front feet."

"This was a mythical ram," I explained, "sent by the god Mercury."

"With a mythical outboard motor stuck up his backside, too, I should reckon."

I ignored the foolish laughter.

"Now Jason sailed in the *Argo* with fifty-three warriors and one woman. She was Atalanta, the famous huntress and runner . . ."

"She had to be," said Private Clapper. "Round and round that deck all day with fifty-three randy warriors after her."

To such steady chy-iking I took C Company over the seas with the Argonauts to Lemnos and the menless women, past Hercules on Cios, leaving behind us Amycus broken-jawed

[57]

and Phineus harpy-freed, and beating through the Clashers to landfall on Colchis. And the whole being rendered in words of two syllables.

"And the king said that Jason must do three things single-handed before he could have the Fleece. He must yoke to the plough the terrible brazen bulls, plough a field with them and sow there the teeth of a dragon. Only then could he try to take the Fleece from the fierce dragon that guarded it."

"I'll lay four-to-one on the dragon."

"Now the king's daughter, Medea, fell in love with Jason and gave him some magic herbs which tamed the bulls. As he sowed the dragon's teeth in the furrows, each one turned into a warrior. But Jason slew them all and sprinkled the magic herbs on the dragon so that it went to sleep. Then he took the Fleece single-handed and sailed away in the *Argo* with Medea . . ."

"And they all lived happy ever after."

"Please, sir, can we have 'Red Riding Hood' tomorrow night?"

Private Parkin rose again.

"Very interesting, sir," he said. "Might we borrow the book for tonight. So that we can study the legend and be sure not to let the major down tomorrow."

"Certainly," I said, handing it over. "Most commendable outlook, Parkin."

We were up at dawn next morning for the advance on the Fleece. Sergeant Major Dickory came hullabalooing to the major.

"It's mutiny, sir. Eighty-one men are refusing to get up."

Private Parkin came out of the signals tent with a message form.

"Top Priority and Personal from General Trugg."

Captain Croker announced it.

"The Divisional Commander expects this day that all troops will model themselves on the glorious example of the Argonauts."

[58]

"And that's all we're trying to do sir," said Private Parkin. "Our only aim is to keep you in good with the general. According to Mr. Goodbody's book there were only fifty-three Argonauts and there's a hundred and thirty-four of us. So we drew lots last night for the honour of assaulting the Golden Fleece and you've got exactly fifty-three volunteer heroes on parade. We wouldn't want the general finding you with a hundred and thirty-four Argonauts on the starting line and thinking you'd never even read the story."

"Fifty-three Argonauts?" shouted Major Arkdust. "Is that right, Mr. Goodbody?"

"Yes, sir, but ..."

"There's no time for buts, we should have been away already. What the hell d'you want to give them these bolshy ideas for?"

"I was only carrying out the general's orders, sir ..."

Everybody shouted at me and ran around in frantic military circles. Captain Croker was all for putting the eighty-one non-volunteers under close arrest for mutiny but the sergeant major calculated that the other fifty-three would have to stay behind to guard them. Then there would be no Argonauts on the objective, a mass court-martial tailor-made for the newspapers and bowler hats flying out all round.

"If I might make a suggestion, sir," said Private Parkin. "It says in the book that Jason left a guard on his boat when he landed at Colchis. It'd be no good getting back to the jetty with the Golden Fleece to find somebody had nicked your *Argo*, would it?"

So the eighty-one layabouts were left as nominal *Argo* guards to be dealt with on return to barracks, and the fifty-three volunteer heroes marched off cursing their ill-luck in the lottery. Three miles later, as we topped the ridge overlooking Hurt Wood, somebody whistled three times and they all sat down.

"What the hell's up now?" bellowed Major Arkdust.

"Begging your pardon, sir," said Private Parkin, "but your

[59]

men wish only to prevent you making a grievous mistake. We don't want to get you in bad with the general by going any farther. The Argonauts didn't do anything about actually taking the Fleece from the dragon." He held out the *Child's Wonder Book*. "You can see here, sir, that Jason did it all single-handed with the help of the old balsam his girl friend, Medea, gave him."

You could see Major Arkdust's lips moving as he read. "By George! But Parkin's dead right. That's just what it says in the book. Where's that ruddy Goodbody. . . . Ah! There you are. . . . If it hadn't been for you and your bolshy lecture last night we'd never have had all this damned trouble . . ."

"I only did, sir, what I thought . . ."

"Single-handed, Mr. Goodbody, you got us into this mess and single-handed you're going to get us out of it. Jason! That's who you are. I hereby appoint you the regimental Jason. Hold out your hand." He took out his tobacco pouch and sprinkled my palm with curly cut.

"There's your magic herbs. And down there are your brazen bulls breathing fire." On the grassland below, fourteen Friesians puffed smoke on the frosty morning air. "The dragon's teeth have already been sown and sprouted warriors." He pointed at the ploughed field around Hurt Wood where hairy-armed Cameronians were already dug in. "So you're on your way, Jason. Get down there in that wood and don't come back without that flaming Fleece."

As I beat it over the ridge and across the field, the Jocks spotted me and set up a bombardment of clods, rocks, and thunderflashes. An assault party rose from the furrows and came after me. I just made the wood, tripped in some sort of badger trap, rolled head-over-heels down a ravine and landed on top of a soldier in a leather jerkin.

"Who the hell are you?" he demanded unravelling the ferns from his face.

My mouth was full of compost, my forelock singed by fire-

[60]

works, my left arm felt broken, and I am afraid I lost my temper.

"I'm Jason," I shouted. "Going in single-handed with my magic herbs to get the Golden Fleece." I showed him my handful of curly cut. He took it and filled his pipe.

"Thank you," he said.

"If Hitler ever hears about this military charade," I blazed on, "he'll die laughing. Next week, we'll be out doing the Three Bears and mock fighting for the biggest bowl of porridge. . . . And who are you? The dragon?"

"Sometimes," he said. He took off his helmet to shake out the last of the bracken and I saw he was General Trugg. I came as smartly to attention as my injuries would allow and saluted.

"I beg your pardon, sir."

"Don't stand there like a blasted waxworks, boy. The Fleece is behind the copper beech. And there's a dozen Jocks with pickaxe handles coming after your blood."

As the Scots came raging down the ravine, I dismissed myself, circled the tree, snatched up the sheepskin and hared back across the fields. Defenders came from the other side of the wood to cut me off. Flagging fast I went up the hill again pursued by two converging columns of maddened Picts. Just as the pincers were about to close upon me fifty-two of the volunteer Argonauts came whooping over the ridge and crashed happily into the Cameronians. The fifty-third hero, Private Parkin, went out to a flank firing Very lights at the rumps of the cows and sending the herd of frenzied Friesians stampeding into the rearguard.

I cleared the crest in safety and staggered, at last gasp, up to Major Arkdust. He was sitting on his shooting stick studying the *Child's Wonder Book*. I dropped the sheepskin in at his feet and collapsed beside it.

"Mission completed, sir," I panted. "Jason reporting with the Golden Fleece."

"Don't lie down, Jason," he said. "I haven't told you you

can stand at ease yet. . . . And where's Medea? She's supposed to be fleeing with you according to the book."

"Hotly pursued, too, by her father, the king of Colchis," I said rising to my dead feet, "and here he comes now, roaring up the hill."

General Trugg had appeared from the wood and was plodding fast across the plough.

"Then we'd better beat it back to the *Argo*."

Major Arkdust blew his whistle, the fifty-three heroes broke off combat and went hotfoot back over the downs. I picked up my greasy, yellow pelt and set my broken bones rolling after them.

Chapter Seven

... I am reminded of the time when I tried to teach Military Law at
Sandhurst and the memory revives my sympathy with the Regimental
Officer who must master the subject. It is easy to say that the Manual
of Military Law contains all that need be known about it, but that is
cold comfort for some of us. . . . There are two main reasons why
an officer should be at home in Military Law. One of them, the less
important, is that he may pass his promotion examinations. The other,
by far the more important, is that he may avoid injustice towards his
fellow-countrymen whom it is his privilege to command . . .

GEN. SIR CHARLES HARRINGTON
Handbook of Military Law

I TOOK MY NEXT STEP up the Army ladder in January 1942,
when after only eighteen months' commissioned service I was
made a full lieutenant. On the day my appointment was published the adjutant sent for me and I marched into his office
with the maturity of a second pip shining on either shoulder.

"Your services have been requested as defending officer,"
said Captain Tablet, "by Private Juniper of B Company who
is at present in the cells awaiting court-martial for being
absent without leave for sixty-seven days. Have you any reason to advance why you should not accept?"

"No, sir."

"Then here is a copy of the summary of evidence and the
rest of the papers. The court sits in a fortnight's time. And
with Goodbody for the defence may the Lord have mercy on
Juniper's misguided soul."

[63]

I was very pleased with my assignment. There had been no opportunity for me to practise in Military Law since I left the O. C. T. U. Fortunately my legal studies were recorded in the second volume of my notebook which had been saved from Major Arkdust and the deep, blue sea. Armed with my notes, the *Manual of Military Law* and *King's Regulations*, I went to see my client in the cells.

He was a little, world-worn nut of a man, a recalled reservist who had seen fifteen years' service and possessed five sheets to his conduct record.

"Tell me, Juniper," I opened, "how did you come to choose me?"

"With a pin, sir. It don't make no difference who I have for prisoner's friend. With that summary and my record, Norman Birkett couldn't get me off the hook."

I had hoped that he had heard of the forensic skill I had shown in dealing with such Twelve Platoon problems as Clapper's insurance difficulty, but resolved not to allow the manner of my selection to deflect me from my duty.

"That's no way to look at it, Juniper. Must keep our pecker up, you know. All prisoners are innocent until proven guilty."

"Not in the Army, they ain't."

"Indeed they are, I assure you. It says so right here in the *Manual of Military Law*. Now what would be our best line of defence?"

"What about suicide?"

"I see you are charged with being absent without leave in Runcorn for sixty-seven days. Why did you go there?"

"I don't know."

"Your record shows you've been guilty of absence without leave on eleven other occasions in the last two and a half years, and always in Runcorn. Why do you keep going back to Runcorn?"

"I don't know."

"You must know. Does your wife live there?"

[64]

"I'm not married."

"Your girl friend?"

"Haven't got one."

"Then what on earth keeps calling you back to Runcorn? Is there something wrong with you?"

Juniper peered apprehensively at me like a man being followed, gazed up at the whitewashed ceiling, then down at his own reflection in the bottom of the bucket he was burnishing.

"It's me head, sir!"

"Your head?"

"Yes, sir. Inside the skull, like. Blackouts, that's what I get, blackouts." He banged his temples with a tortured palm. "Horrible. . . . I'm sitting down somewhere, just like I'm sitting down here with you, sir, when suddenly all the inside of me head goes black. I get this feeling that I got to get out of the barrack room. I got to roam, if you know what I mean. I feel all sort of . . . sort of . . ."

"Nomadic?" I suggested.

"That's it, sir. I come all over sort of nomadic." The traumatic barrier having been broken, he opened his heart to me. "Plop! Something goes plop between me ears and I'm all blacked-out and nomadic. Everything seems to close in around me. The barrack blocks, the cookhouse, the windows and the walls, they all come marching in on me and I just got to get out in the fresh air . . ." His black button eyes popped hysterically and his arms flailed about like a man locked in a submarine. "I just got to go off travelling. . . . I don't know what I'm doing. . . . I don't know where I'm going. . . . I just wander in a trance, helpless as a sleepwalker, maybe for hours, maybe for days, until the attack wears off and I wake up in Runcorn."

"Always in Runcorn?"

"Yes." He spread his hands in resignation. "Always in Runcorn."

"And how often do you have these nomadic blackouts?"

[65]

"All the time, sir. I never know when I'm going to be took."

He buried his face in his hands.

"Oh! Gawd! Will it never end!"

Fortunately, I knew a little about psychiatry as well as insurance. Not, mark you, any of that Freudian stuff about sex and all that, but enough for me to recognize that I might well have before me a case of obsessive nomadism.

"Now, bear up, Juniper," I said, inclining one shoulder towards him so that he might take confidence from the seniority of my second pip. "I'm here to defend you. Never fear but that the truth shall out. I will study the papers and see you again tomorrow."

A brilliant idea was brewing at the back of my mind, just a glimpse of the foundation upon which the edifice of defence might be built. I've no doubt Perry Mason often had the same sensation. I had, of course, filed with my War Memoirs material a copy of the battalion orders in which my promotion had been published. Down at the bottom of the second page was a reminder to all medical officers about the importance of the latest Army Council Instruction which bade them keep an eye out for any cases of porcyliocosis. Any cases found had to be reported immediately to the Director General. I had read up the A. C. I., just in case there might be an outbreak of the disease in Twelve Platoon. Porcyliocosis afflicted people who had eaten diseased pork over a long period and was therefore occasionally to be found among soldiers who had served in India where the pigmeat tends towards the putrid. The symptoms visited on the sufferer, many years after he had digested the pork and forgotten it, consisted of unheralded mental blackouts, loss of memory and wandering somnambulism.

I took the A. C. I. to the guard room and explained it to Juniper.

"This may be the cause of all this Runcorn trouble," I

[66]

said. "You may be a porcyliocosis sufferer. Tell me, now, did you ever eat diseased pork during your service in India?"

His face lit up. I had clearly struck chords in his memory.

"All the time, sir. The cook sergeant in India was a dead villian. Never served us nothing but diseased pork every day. I remember it well, now you come to remind me. It was the midday sun as curdled it. All greenlooking and crawling with maggots, it was. Done up nauseating day after day with gravy thick and sweet potatoes. Fair turns me up to think of it. . . . Ugh! . . . Quetta, Peshawar, Jellybad . . . everywhere we soldiered, never nothing for dinner but diseased pork."

Captain Truffle, M.B., Medical Officer to the Fourth Musketeers was young, tubby, and bursting with surgical ambition. His eyes glistened as I described my client's service, symptoms, and Indian pork consumption.

"By George!" he said, "but it all checks with the A.C.I. Special report to be made to the Director General, too. Very rare, you know, cases of porcyliocosis. Wonderful thing if we had one in the regiment."

On the way to the cells I told him that Captain Tablet would be prosecuting the case. Truffle and the adjutant were daggers drawn, a relationship which had its base in the doctor's belief that the excessive stamping softened the brain and overexposure to whitewash hardened the arteries.

"Tablet is it?" he said. "Just the sort of thing he'd enjoy doing—hounding a chap who's not medically responsible for his actions."

He questioned Juniper for an hour or so and jabbed him in all sorts of unusual places in search of reflexes. Juniper had asked me the previous day for a copy of the A.C.I. so that he could check his symptoms against the official description and all his answers seemed sadly satisfying to Captain Truffle. He finally closed his notebook, gave the elastic a triumphant snap and took me with him into the corridor for specialist consultation.

[67]

"That man certainly fits the bill. On all the counts given in the instruction he's a porcyliocosis suspect. I'll start on my report right away. I'll write a letter to the *Lancet,* too. Maybe to *The Times* as well. A paper on porcyliocosis could really put the Musketeers on the medical map."

I broke the news of his plight to Juniper and he took it very bravely. There were four days left before the court-martial and I spent many hours with him going over the details of our defence, which claimed that his absences were due to mental blackouts and nomadic somnambulism caused by pig poisoning.

He was a natural actor and a perfectionist at rehearsal. I don't know what line of business Juniper went into after the war but the Method school of acting could well have had its genesis behind the guard room of the Fourth Musketeers. Since neither of us had yet seen another case of porcyliocosis, he was uninhibited in his display of outward symptoms.

"I'll wear my Army glasses on the day, sir," he decided. "They always seem to give people a dodgy look." He put on his flat-sided aluminium spectacles and the pebble lenses focused his beady, black eyeballs as eerily as any vulture. I supposed it was the strain of waiting for the trial which developed the nervous tic in his neck muscles. Every fifteen seconds his left eye would wink, the sinister side of his mouth twitch, and his head jerk sideways like an ageing importuner pressed for time.

On the morning of the court-martial he loped in between his escorts with the leg action of Groucho Marx and the head roll of Fagin. He had put on his makeup for the occasion, whitening his face with scouring powder and darkening his eye pouches with laundry bluing. He sat down on the extreme edge of his chair, his knees tightly closed as a desperate virgin, arms folded Sioux fashion across his chest, withdrawn and silent as a zombie in battle dress, his brooding immobility broken only by the regular grimace of his quarter-minute tic.

Even I, who had watched him in rehearsal, was shaken by the quality of his first-night performance. And the three members of the court were visibly affected. The president, Major Cutts-Bodlin, surveyed his defendant through a startled monocle and the down turning of his moustache indicated his conviction that he had caught a right one here. Captain Pebble from the Lancers came bolt upright in his chair and set to nodding like a slack-jawed metronome in time to the twitch. Lieutenant Comb, the junior member, opposite whom the spectre was seated, edged nervously back from the table and when Juniper looked up at him and groaned miserably, I thought he was going to run away.

"Well," said the major, turning his gaze steadfastly away from the prisoner, "we'd better get started."

It was his first court-martial presidency and he was a long time working through the formal preliminaries.

"Now," he said. "Private Juniper, you've heard the charge made against you. How do you plead? Guilty or not guilty?"

I stood up.

"The defence wishes, sir, to put forward a plea in bar of trial."

"Oh! You do, do you? . . . Plea in bar of trial, eh?"

He had clearly not met such an opening gambit before and went scurrying through the pages of his little green book, the *Child's Guide to Court-Martial Procedure*. After a whispered conference with Captain Pebble he found the right paragraph.

"Ah . . . yes. . . . In bar of trial. . . . And on what grounds does the defence raise such a plea?"

"On the grounds, sir, that due to infirmities occasioned while on active service the prisoner was not responsible for the actions leading to the charges made against him and is medically unfit for trial."

[69]

"Medically unfit? What's wrong with him?"

"He has, sir, the dreaded porcyliocosis."

"Porcyliocosis?" He looked at his fellow members, at Captain Tablet, at the escort; but no one could help him.

"What's porcylio-what's-its-name?"

"As you will recall, sir, it is the disease described in Army Council Instruction 903 of 1942 which causes mental blackouts and nomadic somnambulism."

"Is it? And how'd he get it?"

I drew myself to my full height.

"By eating diseased pork in India."

"Eating what?" His monocle clattered to the table from his unsprung face.

"Diseased pork." I breathed on my fingernails and polished them nonchalantly on my lapel. "It's all in the A.C.I., sir."

That had him right over the legal barrel. To have the Army Council backing the defence with an edict they'd never even read put the court in a rare tizzy. Finally, after much puffing and blowing, the major adjourned the proceedings while Captain Tablet, swearing sibilantly, went off to get him a copy of A.C.I. 903/42. And by the time he'd found it, the court had read it, and I had dilated upon its relevance, it was time for lunch.

Opening the afternoon session, the president announced that the court noted the content of the A.C.I. and desired to know what evidence there was to prove that the prisoner suffered from the relevant disease.

"Damned sprucer!" snorted Captain Tablet who was accustomed to his courts-martial finishing before lunch. "Malingering, that's what it is. Wasting everybody's time with a cock-and-bull story. Ought to have him medically examined."

"Which," I said, "the defence has already done. My first witness is the medical officer."

Captain Truffle didn't help the adjutant's composure by refusing to take the oath.

"What's your objection?" asked the president. "Are you Mohammedan or something?"

"Give him a plate to break," muttered the prosecutor.

"I am here to offer medical opinion, not to state facts. Such expert evidence is normally given without oath."

"Never heard anything like it in my life," fumed Tablet. "Everybody has to take the oath."

"If you're an adjutant," said Truffle, "you should read the *Manual.*"

Their animosity sparked back and forth until Major Cutts-Bodlin asserted his authority and sent them to their corners. He riffled wearily through his books and finally pronounced that the doctor was perfectly right.

Pompous in victory, Truffle settled down to read a five thousand word paper on porcyliocosis, his letter to the *Lancet,* his case notes on Private Juniper, and the second draft of his report to the Director General. After two and a half hours of medical droning he closed with his opinion "that the court should not rule out the possibility that the prisoner has contracted porcyliocosis and that his absences were committed during mental blackouts resulting from that disease."

This ended the first day and I felt pardonable satisfaction with the progress of the defence. My client was somewhat put out, however, because Truffle and I had taken all the verbal limelight.

"When am I going to get my chance," he demanded. "I'm getting browned off just sitting there like a stone-deaf Buddha."

He got his chance next day and took it with both hands. After a morning of Tablet-Truffle bickering, in which the adjutant kept throwing up his hands and demanding of the heavens, "But why Runcorn every time? Just tell me that. Why always Runcorn?" and the doctor kept doggedly repeating his expert opinion in reply, I sent Juniper into action.

[71]

"Now tell the court," I said, "in your own words, the details of your service."

He was superb. Irving and his Bells, Chaliapin and his Flea, Olivier and Crookback, all paled to parish hall charades against Juniper and the deadly pork. He leaned forward, lowered his crouch and held out his arms to gather the court's attention. He took them sadly through his childhood as the ninth infant of a bibulous glassblower in Stalybridge whose working life was mainly unemployed because the drink affected his puff and his intended jeroboams kept turning out gills. Driven to the Colours by equal portions of hunger and patriotism, he took service as a drummer boy and shifted uneasily on his seat as he recalled the impact on his young mind of his friendship with a corporal trombonist of oriental tastes.

". . . when I was nineteen the battalion sailed for India and went into action up on the Northwest Frontier. Up against the wily Pathan, we was, sir, dead cruel, no mercy and the sun beating down all the time on the rocks and the back of your head and them vast, stony wastes . . ." He gasped for water, dry-mouthed as an Afghan beggar, and held up pitiful hands to protect his head from the brazen sun.

"All over the mountains we marched, Quetta to Peshawar, Kashmir to Jellybad, fighting and camping, camping and fighting, all the time eating that horrible pork . . . day in, day out. . . . Pork . . . pork . . . pork . . . nothing else but pork. All that heat and flies and nowhere for the cooks to wash their hands and pigs everywhere going down like ninepins with the infectious Indian swine-plague. A-crawling with grubs, a loin of pork could move off while you watched it. You could smell your way to the cook house by day and at night you could pick it out by the pigmeat's luminous glow. . . . Ugh! It was horrible . . . but it was all we had. . . . It was eat that diseased pork or starve. . . . I can taste it now, like cannibal's gorgonzola."

Lieutenant Comb turned a delicate green and dusted a handkerchief over his mouth.

"And after a while it began to affect me up here." Juniper knocked his head with his knuckles and cast up the whites of his eyes like a corpse. "I began to get them wandering blackouts. I'd be sitting there in the camp and the night'd just be coming down and getting all misty and shadowy. And then everything would start closing in on me. The hills would come marching down, the tents'd start moving in . . ." He crouched deep into his shoulders for protection and his hypnotized audience crouched with him. "The canvas'd come flapping closer and closer . . . nearer and nearer . . . everything crowding down on me . . . squeezing me tighter and tighter. . . . Them drums'd start beating inside me head . . . boom, boom, boom, boom . . ."

His fist thudded tom-toms on the arm of his chair and every head jerked in obedience to the rhythm. His breathing grew heavy as a medium, his voice a-tremble with tension.

"Everything trying to smother me . . . choking me . . . suffocating me. Drums getting louder and louder . . . busting out the bones of me skull. . . . I got to escape . . . I got to get away before it's too late . . . before I go mad! Boom! Boom! Boom! Boom! And then just when flesh and blood can't stand no more there's that great yellow and red explosion behind me eyes . . . ker-ploish! . . . And then everything goes silent and black and I'd wake up hours later, days later, weeks later, sitting in some Wog village miles and miles away and me feet cut to ribbons . . ."

He caressed the soles of his boots tenderly and held them out for sympathetic inspection.

"And it kept on happening to me. Every now and then I'd have a blackout and wake up somewhere in the jungle. And all the time nothing to eat but that mouldy pork . . . pork chops, salt pork, leg of pork, sausages and all the lot dead crawling and rotten. When we went into cantonments it got worse. All the huts'd come marching in on me . . . then there'd be the old rainbow explosion and they'd find me Gawd knows how long later sitting in a trance in some distant bazaar. And back in England it's been just the same. . . . I'd be sitting there in the barrack room of an evening doing domestic economy when suddenly the barrack blocks started marching in on me . . . the walls start closing down . . . the beds come round and pen me up. . . I can't move . . . I can't breathe . . ." He screwed himself up like a hedgehog and clawed despairingly at his throat. "I can't hear . . . I can't see. . . . And then everything bursts up in the air again. . . . Me legs work but I can't control them . . . I have to wander. I can't stop. I'm driven on and on, this way, that way, walking, walking, walking, until at last I wake up again . . . deadbeat . . . done up . . . in Runcorn." At the name of the fateful town he collapsed in a dead faint, lifeless but for his shuddering twitch, an artist to the end, limp, exhausted, and streaming with thespian sweat.

Lieutenant Comb tottered from the room, handkerchief tight to his lips. Captain Pebble rapidly drank three glasses of water. Major Cutts-Bodlin fanned himself with the summary of evidence and ordered another adjournment while the prisoner was taken out into the fresh air.

"Chuck a bucket of water over him," said Captain Tablet. "Scrim-shanker!"

"Get a stretcher," retorted Captain Truffle, "and take him to the M.I. room."

Four of the idle prosecution witnesses were pressed into service as stretcher-bearers, and Juniper was borne unconscious from the scene of his triumph. An hour later, he raised a tremulous head, gazed wild-eyed around and asked, "Where am I? Is it Runcorn again?" The doctor insisted that he rest before returning to trial and it was after four when we all got settled in the courtroom again.

"During the adjournment," said the president, "the court

[74]

has considered the evidence so far and has decided that specialist opinion on the prisoner's condition is required. Arrangements have, therefore, been made for him to be examined by a psychiatrist at Porthley Hospital tomorrow morning. The court will be adjourned until the specialist's opinion is available."

I was delighted. We were clearly winning. It had been two long days but the court now accepted the porcyliocosis possibility. Once you got the head-shrinker in for the defence, you were as good as home and dried. I travelled with Juniper to the hospital next morning.

"I copped the film show last night," he said. "You can see it from the guard room windows. Smashing it was. *The Hunchback of Notre Dame*. That Charles Laughton fair brought tears to your eyes as Quasimodo."

He beguiled the journey by reenacting scenes from the *Hunchback*, twisting up one shoulder and leering hideously over it with his black-bagged eyes. I left him at Major Spragworthy's door.

"Tell the psychiatrist your story the way you told it to the court, Juniper, and you'll be a free man."

He gave me the big thumbs-up.

"Don't you worry, sir. I'll slay him. I've learnt a new trick or two from Charles Laughton."

And he hobbled over the threshold, adding a Quasimodo lurch to the horror of his Groucho-Fagin gait. I sat in the waiting room till he came out an hour later.

"How did it go?"

"Marvellous. Laid him properly in the aisle. I'm really getting into the part now, if you know what I mean."

"You were a long time."

"That was him. I got my story over in twenty minutes. The rest of the time he spent trying to get me to fix square pegs into round holes and do kids' jigsaws and all that stuff."

"And how did you get on?"

[75]

He laid a cagey finger alongside his nose.

"He wasn't catching me that way. I was on to his game all right. I did all his tests wrong."

The court resumed next day and Major Spragworthy gave his report. He had a nervous tic worse than Juniper's. I supposed he caught it from a patient. His specialist rank demanded he be even more long-winded than Truffle and he ambled patronizingly through his theory of porcyliocosis, described his examination in detail and remarked on the interesting features he had found in the Juniper case. He was obviously coming our way and I relaxed happily as he came at last to his peroration.

". . . and after consideration of all the available medical evidence I would first advise the court that there are clear indications that the prisoner may be suffering from porcyliocosis."

We'd made it! Juniper came out of his zombiecrouch and gave the V-sign all round. I smiled sympathetically at the defeated adjutant.

". . . and furthermore," went on the specialist, "in the light of his reactions during my examination and his abnormal performance of standard psychiatric tests, there are grounds for suspecting a background of hereditary insanity. While mental degeneration may not yet have reduced him to a state in which he is clearly certifiable, I feel that he should be transferred to a mental hospital for special observation over a long period to ascertain whether certification may not, at this stage, be in his own best interests. . . ."

And he went on to make it painfully clear that he thought my client should be put away. The moment the last deadly syllable left his lips I asked for an adjournment. As Major Spragworthy left he gave me an old-fashioned look. If he hadn't had that tic, I would have sworn he winked our way. Juniper and I retired for consultation.

"Strike a bloody light, sir," he said, "but you've done me

proud as defending officer. If we'd pleaded guilty four days ago I'd likely have got fifty-six days. Now they want to put me in the looney-bin for life."

"It's your own fault, Juniper. You overplayed your part. It was all that Quasimodo stuff that did it. You should never have put in that hunchback business."

"What are we going to do now? You're going to get me certified bleeding insane. I'd sooner do a stretch in the glass-house than the madhouse, any day."

"Now easy up, Juniper. Don't despair. I'll see you through."

"You'll see me out of that courtroom in a ruddy strait-jacket, that's what you'll do. This time tomorrow they'll have me in the rubber room with no belt, braces, nor bootlaces."

"They will not," I said decisively. "We still have a line of retreat."

The court reassembled wearily. The tribunal was fraying badly at the edges. I rose to my feet.

"The defence now wishes to withdraw its plea in bar of trial and accepts that the prisoner was responsible for his actions during his repeated visits to Runcorn. . . . We now plead Guilty."

Major Cutts-Bodlin groaned and covered his face with his hands. On emerging he gestured at the pile of foolscap on which he had recorded the proceedings. His mouth opened and shut four times before he could raise a sounding word.

"Four days," he grated. "Four days you keep this court sitting here while you try to make out that the prisoner has some form of human swine-fever. Six witnesses you keep kicking their heels in the corridor for four days and not one of them has yet spoken a single word. The prosecuting officer has been kept all this time from his official duties, the court warrant officer and escorts have been uselessly confined between these four walls, Captain Pebble has missed his regimental point-to-point, and Lieutenant Comb, who was

[77]

hoping to be married yesterday, has had to postpone the ceremony. . . . Four days! Eighteen men! I calculate, Lieutenant Goodbody, that you have deprived your country in time of war of no less than seventy-two man-days, you have forced me to compile thirty-seven pages of useless proceedings, you have kept this court in purgatory for ninety-six hours listening to a rigmarole of medical poppycock, and at the end of that time you have the damned brass-necked temerity to stand there and say you now plead Guilty!" His voice rose to a frenzied yell and he hammered his fist on the table sending his thirty-seven pages to the four winds. "Do you know what you are?"

"No, sir."

"You're a damned Fifth Columnist, that's what you are! A blasted saboteur! If you can plead guilty now why couldn't you do so at ten o'clock last Monday and save everybody four days of their lives?"

I made no answer. I just couldn't think of anything soothing to say. He raved at me for a long time and I stood there in silence and took it all on the bony part of the forehead. Captain Pebble took over when his president tired and told me at length that I needed pig-sticking. Lieutenant Comb spoke with such bitterness about his delayed marriage that I could only presume his young lady was pregnant. Captain Tablet puffed messages of hate and threats of future revenge from underneath his moustache and murdered me with his eyes. And Private Juniper, when the court had finally settled down and awarded him 182 days, refused to have me inside his cell to discuss an appeal on the grounds that the members of the tribunal were overwrought and unjustly biased against him.

As I left the guard room, disappointed of course, but comforted by the knowledge that I had done my best for my client, Private Clapper accosted me.

"Begging your pardon, sir, and all that, but could I have a few words with you on a compassionate matter?"

[78]

"Certainly, Clapper," I said. "What's the trouble this time?"

"It's my missus again, sir. They're all after her again."

"Not that insurance man? I thought we cleared him out when we lapsed the funeral policy."

He smiled bravely.

"You done him, all right, sir. Settled his hash proper. It ain't him this time. It's the butcher."

"The butcher? And do I take it that he is now ... ahem ... committing intimacy at your home address?"

"Yes, sir. Comes round regular every Tuesday with a bit of meat off the ration. Weakens her self-control with steak and kidney, he does, lures her with liver till she's that hungry she don't know what he's up to. My mum's told him off about it, but he don't take no notice. He just won't leave that poor little kid alone. It's getting on my nerves, and if somebody don't do something about it soon I'm going to finish up a raving lunatic in Runcorn like old Juniper in there. Is it right, sir, that's all I want to know for civilian butchers to go round getting their hoggins off soldiers' wives while they're away fighting gallantly for their King and Country ..."

"Now don't take on, Clapper. We'll find a way to discourage the butcher, don't you worry. Tell me, is there any chance that you could persuade your wife and your mum to become vegetarians?"

Before he could reply Sergeant Transom came up at the double.

"Urgent message from the company commander, sir. Special order group right away."

I left Clapper considering female vegetarianism and hurried off to the company office.

"What's it all about, Sergeant?"

"Don't let on I told you, sir, because it's supposed to be top secret, but we're off next week."

"Off where?"

[79]

"North Africa, for a quid."

"How do you know?"

"The quartermaster's just received five hundred pairs of snow boots and the M.O.'s lumbered up with fourteen crates of frostbite ointment. It's us for the desert sands, sure as drainholes."

And he was just about right.

Chapter Eight

... In February we received information that the enemy was preparing for a more ambitious counter-attack against our lines than he had yet attempted. To provide additional strength for this attack some of Rommel's forces were hurried back from Tripoli to join von Arnim and Messe in Tunisia. Watchfulness was of course indicated everywhere ...

GEN. DWIGHT D. EISENHOWER
Crusade in Europe

AFTER BRINGING TWELVE PLATOON ashore at Cleptha and exploiting the good fortune of our unopposed landing, I pushed on along the coast road towards Tunis, as anxious as the rest of the chaps to get our first crack at the Boche. From the icy welcome we were given by the Colonial French some of them would clearly have preferred us to have been the Boche. Nevertheless, we conferred upon them in passing the benison of liberation which included among its favours the use of their daughters, the requisition of their wine, and the passage of tanks through their vineyards. The Musketeers pressed on in traditional style and we would have been in Tunis by Christmas had we not actually met the Germans on the way.

We then, of course, had to stop and withdraw a little; the rains came down, the mud squelched a foot deep, and the Army settled in to hold a line forty miles from Tunis and await attack weather and dry going in the spring. When the sun began to shine in March 1943, C Company was in the

[81]

line just north of Medjez-el-Bab dug in around a farm on the
ungrateful slopes of Djebel Tokurna. Between the ribbons of
rock the earth dried to grey dust, and but for a few stunted
corktrees and twisted olives, the farmer grew nothing but
stones. There was a riverless valley of similar fertility and
broken by dry *wadis*, which stretched for half a mile to the
facing hills which were occupied by the Boche. Major Arkdust summoned his commanders to an order group in the
scullery of the farmhouse.

"Preparations are being made at Army Headquarters for a
big attack to break through to Tunis. Since the planning staff
have to make twenty-six copies of everything, they can't do
the job in five minutes. It'll take them even longer than
usual here, of course, because the dear chaps have to work
three hundred miles away in Algiers. Even at that distance,
from the smell of gunpowder they sense that the Germans
may also be planning an attack. They would like the earliest
possible warning if this is so, in order, no doubt, that they
may withdraw to previously prepared positions in Rio de
Janeiro. We are, therefore, instructed during the interim period to intensify our patrolling with two objects—one, to become familiar with the terrain between ourselves and the
enemy in preparation for our possible attack, and two, to
observe the enemy and detect as early as possible any sign of
impending counterattack. We will now take each platoon's
sector in detail . . ."

Later, back at my platoon headquarters in a disused pull-
up for goats, Sergeant Transom surveyed the German hills
through his binoculars.

"If I was Jerry I'd not bother coming across here. He's got
just as good a load of stones on his *djebel* as we've got on
ours."

"His main position is around that sugarloaf, Djebel
Aboudir. From his side, whoever holds that has got the valley. Our main task is to reconnoitre a possible route up there.

[82]

And to watch whether he shows any intention of coming down."

He studied the spot for a while.

"The more you stare at it," he said, "the less you see. It's loaded with false crests and crisscrossed with *wadis*. We'll have to patrol down at night to get any sort of idea."

The flat central bed of the valley was commanded by both sides and there was no possibility of unscreened movement across it by day. On four nights we patrolled across, but could never get any real idea of the going around Djebel Aboudir. The first patrol caught a trip-wire, set up a Boche flare, and spent three hours crouching in a heaven-sent hole while spandaus plastered their neighbourhood. The second found a German patrol already working its beat; on the third we became hopelessly lost among the *wadis* at the foot of the hill and the last, which made some progress across them, was defeated by dawn and an apparently unscalable chasm.

A flexible mind is an essential attribute of a good commander. He should always be prepared to change his approach if his initial plans do not bring success. I sat down quietly and thought our problem through. Then I called my subordinate commanders together.

"It is clear," I said, "that we are not going to find out much about Djebel Aboudir by night."

"And nobody's getting down there in one piece by day," said Sergeant Transom.

"If someone could get into the valley in daylight and up to the gorge that stopped us last night, he'd probably be able to see the best way up the hill."

"If he had any peepers left to see with," said Corporal Dooley. "There's not a scrap of cover between here and the *wadis*."

"But he might get down there without cover," I said. "Some of *them* do."

I pointed to an Arab riding his donkey along the track to

[83]

our rear. His wife was walking in front with the luggage, a battle area reversal of the traditional order of march in order that the spouse could serve as a forward mine detector. The occasional itinerant Arab wandered into the no-man's-land valley apparently to dig stones. Both sides being short of ammunition, we took little notice unless the wanderer turned towards either slope, when a burst over his head sent him scampering terror stricken over the rocks.

"Wogs may do it, sir," said Corporal Hink, "but you'd never get nothing out of them. They don't speak no known language. And Jerry soon shoots them up if they make for the *djbel*."

"That's because they do it in the open. There's plenty of cover among the *wadis* that a trained soldier could use to get a decent O.P."

"And how are you going to turn a Wog into a trained soldier?"

"I'm not. But we could turn a trained soldier into a Wog."

They looked at me in amazement. Their untrained minds had not been able to make so swift an analysis of the situation.

"Do you mean, sir," said Sergeant Transom, "that you want somebody to dress up as a Wog and do a Lawrence of Arabia?"

"Yes. One brave volunteer could then achieve more in ten minutes than ten nights of patrol."

"One brave volunteer?"

"Yes. He should, of course, be an N.C.O. A private soldier would not be capable of the reconnaissance required."

I waited confidently for all four of them to volunteer.

"I'd be in there like a shot," said Corporal Hink, "but you'd never make a Wog out of me with this mop." He ruffled up his Harpo mass of straw-blond hair.

"Same here," said Corporal Globe, "but I can't see across the room if I take off my glasses. And whoever saw a stone-digging Wog in horn-rimmed glasses?"

"And there's no man I'd let be down there before me," said Corporal Dooley, "if it weren't that there's six foot and over fifteen stone of me. There's not one of these Wogs that weigh more than a whippet and Jerry would never believe the size of me in a burnous."

"And I'd not be able to deceive them neither," said Sergeant Transom standing as straight-backed as Queen Mary. "After twenty years of drill parade, I could never drop myself into the proper Wog civilian slouch. You could dress me up in all the bed sheets and bath towels in Bolton and the Boche'd still pick me out as a regular soldier. I'm afraid, sir, I just haven't got the necessary histrionic ability. I have to confess I'm just not up to the job." He shook his head in sad, professional defeat. "And if you don't mind my offering my opinion, sir, there's only one person here with the right figure, acting ability, and natural bearing to play Lawrence of Arabia. . . . Just look at him, boys."

And with a gesture of an impresario, he pointed at me.

"You're dead right, Sergeant," said Corporal Hink admiringly. "Just look at them noble, hawklike features. Spitting image of an Arab sheikh with anaemia."

"And that carriage!" said Corporal Globe. "Just a pale-faced son of the desert. A bit of brown boot polish over your gob, sir, and you could have just stepped off a camel."

"If Mrs. Lawrence ever see you sudden, sir, she'd reckon it was her own boy come back," said Corporal Dooley. "When you get sunburned there's going to be Bedouin bints from all over Arabia coming after you. No doubt about it, sir, you're the dead ringer for the job."

I must confess that I had cast myself in this particular operation as planner rather than executant, bearing in mind that my training and experience would be of more value to the war effort in interpreting the information than in obtaining it. However, now that I looked around my subordinates I could see that it would be difficult to make any of them into convincing Arabs. And since they drew attention to my re-

[85]

semblance to Lawrence of Arabia—I feel this was as much in reference to my qualities of leadership as it was to any mere physical similarity—and I had suggested the daylight idea, there was nothing else I could do but carry it out myself.

The following night I was fitted out in burnous and head-dress, face and hands done brown with an infusion of cigarettes in tea, and equipped with an authentic North African stone-cultivating shovel.

"Anywhere from ten yards up you'd pass for a Wog wonderful, sir," said Sergeant Transom. "You'll be all right for Jerry but what'll you do if you meet some other Wogs down in the *wadis* and they want to pass the time of day?"

"I will make out I'm deaf and dumb. That's what spies always do."

"And have you got that phosphorus bomb?"

"In my burnous pocket."

"Good. Any trouble, you toss that and we'll start piling down the smoke. And don't try getting too close. Remember what happened to Lawrence of Arabia when he tried this gimmick on the Turks."

I went down with a patrol two hours before dawn and hid up in the *wadis*. Tunisians are not, unfortunately, early risers and I had to wait till nine o'clock in the morning before making a move. I was out of view of Djebel Aboudir, screened by a precipitous bluff which bulged out at its foot, but I took the precaution of stopping every ten yards or so to dig a few innocent stones. Steadily, industriously, I worked my way along the sheltered flank of the bluff to its extremity, around which I would leave its cover and come into full view on the open plain. The last twenty yards ran through a rock-strewn gully backed by caves running under the bluff. I scrambled round a boulder as big as a bus and stopped dead in my nightgown as an Arab came round the corner ahead!

He stopped and looked at me. I applied my shovel to the ground vigorously. It was solid rock around me and the blade

[86]

skated harmlessly back and forth with the sound of a cast iron zither. The Arab lowered his spade and cultivated stones at his own feet. He was luckier than I; he struck gravel.

We worked away for a minute or two and I watched him carefully out of the corner of my eye. He was a small, thin Wog and I calculated I could handle him if it came to fisticuffs. I moved a little closer till we were under ten yards apart and I had a patch of diggable scree to work on. He stopped shovelling and looked at me. Then he grinned, nodded his head happily and spread his arms in friendship. He waited with ear cocked for me to speak.

It was a good job I had thought the thing through to my deaf-and-dumb act. I placed the tips of my fingers on my lips, shook my head in hopeless negative and fanned my palms before my face like an umpire signalling a washout. I made the motions three times, then transferred to my ears and repeated the triple pantomime. In final emphasis I stood motionless, my spade at ease, and opened and closed my mouth soundlessly in the fashion of a fish mimic.

The Arab was at first taken aback by my actions, and obvious alarm spread across his semitic features. Then he got my message, his grin returned and he nodded understandingly. To my amazement he put his shovel to the ground and gave a repeat performance of my own mouth, ears, and goldfish charade. At the end of his act he pointed vigorously at me and then back at himself and I took his meaning. . . . He was deaf and dumb, too!

Accustomed as I am to find that anyone of whom I ask the way turns out to be stone-deaf or a stranger in the place, I must admit to being utterly surprised that on the only occasion I ever impersonated a dumb soundproof Arab in the interests of His Majesty's Government, the first person I met under Djebel Aboudir turned out to be a Tunisian deafmute.

I returned to digging, to give myself time to think out my

next move, and he did the same. His blade momentarily jammed against some obstinate strata, he slipped in effort and fell on his side. Quickly, he regained his feet, grinning reassurance. . . . I froze suddenly in mid-swing. . . . As his robe swung up in the tumble, a foot had shown clear of the skirt . . . and it was wearing a German field boot!

He was a Boche in disguise, bent on the same errand as myself . . . that's why he'd used my deaf-and-dumb routine. . . . He couldn't speak Arabic either. . . . I kept the shovel going with my left hand while I moved my right stealthily under my gown and drew my revolver. . . . I dropped the shovel and turned to face him.

"*Hände hoch!*" I snapped in all the German I could muster. "*Ich habe sie* covered from beneath my burnous."

He spun round like a duellist and dropped into a fighting crouch.

"*Hände hoch!*" I repeated, bringing my pistol into view. "*Du bist mein* prisoner."

Feverishly, as fast as his hands could flicker, he went through my speak-no-evil, hear-no-evil gestures . . . keeping up the bluff to the end. . . . His right hand came out of pantomime and down to his waist . . . he was reaching for his Luger, but it was under the robe.

"Keep *die Hände* out of your burnous. *Oder ich* shoot to kill."

He was the first German I had ever met in personal combat, face to face. It always goes against the grain for a Britisher to shoot even a Boche in cold blood and it becomes doubly difficult when he's got himself done up like a damned chocolate-coloured cocoon. But total war is a brutal affair . . . it was his life or mine. I shoved my trusty Smith and Wesson farther forward lest it kick back at me and steeled myself to shoot him down like a dog. . . . There was a flutter of white behind him and two Arabs came creeping out of a cave in the bluff. . . . From their postures they were clearly bent on attacking the German from behind. . . . Doubtless, I reasoned, gallant, pro-British Arabs ever-faithful to the Raj. . . . I only had to keep his attention my way and I would have him without bloodshed . . . a dead prisoner can only be identified, a live one can be interrogated.

"Ich gebe sie ein last chance," I said. *"Kamerad! Oder du bist ein* dead man."

His field boots scrabbled on the rocks as he turned to run back round the bluff . . . but the Arabs leapt on him from either side and laid him senseless with a swat from a leather cosh.

"Well done, O faithful Bedouin," I cried and was just going forward to shake their hands when I smelt two more of them close behind me . . . as I turned my head in welcome, someone hit it with a sandbag . . . the scree leapt up to meet me and I went down among silent fireworks into final darkness.

When I awoke I was lying on my back and deep red light was streaming in through a Gothic window. For a moment, in my white draperies, I wondered if I had gone to Heaven. But then, as I raised my head, dull pain spread from the new bump at the back and I saw that I was looking out through the mouth of a cave to the sun going down behind the hills. I tried to get up but I was tied hand and foot. The weight of my belt and revolver was gone from my waist.

The German lay at the back of the cave, hog-tied as I was and still unconscious. There were no Arab brigands in the cave nor, as far as I could see, any outside. In spite of my headache I made a quick appreciation of my military situation. . . . All was not lost. If I could get loose before the German awoke or the Arabs returned, there was still a chance of ultimate victory. I might not have had sight of Djebel Aboudir, but I would have a ready-bound prisoner to take in for interrogation.

First I had to get my hands free. I looked carefully around

for any of the traditional devices. It was an exceptionally bare cave and the Lone Ranger would have been hard up for a bond-loosener. There were no fire embers to char with, no broken bottles to chafe against, no faithful dog with intelligent teeth, and every rock I rubbed my rope on crumbled away as I grated. I twisted and writhed in the dust but my knots had been tied with Arabian cunning and I could make no slack anywhere. I blew myself up and let myself down as I had read in a book about Houdini but succeeded only in raising a raw patch under my neck halter.

After twenty minutes private wrestling my burnous was soaked in sweat and, if anything, my bonds felt tighter. I was getting nowhere inside the cave and decided to look for a knot-pick outside. I rolled myself over and over to the entrance and the phosphorus bomb came out of my pocket as a spear-headed rock ground chips off my hips. I was all set to cast myself vertically over the lip and down into the *wadi* when I caught in the failing light a glimpse of white robe flickering among the rocks. . . . It was the Arabs coming back. . . . There were four of them and it looked as though the Goodbody story was coming to a close. . . . I resolved to sell myself dearly and managed to work my feet round the bomb. I was engaged in trying to lever myself in the manner of a mangonel when the enemy came stalking up to the bluff and into my full view. . . . There was something peculiar about them. . . . They were a very strangely assorted quartet of Wogs . . . their leader stiff as a ramrod in his flapping gown, the second the size of the French second row and bursting his burnous at the seams, the third with yellow hair bushing out of his hood and the fourth wearing horn-rimmed glasses. . . . My faithful N.C.O.'s had come *en masse* to find their lost commander!

"It'll be in one of these caves for sure," said the voice of Corporal Dooley.

"Or maybe buried under one of them piles of rocks," said Corporal Hink.

[90]

"More likely in some sort of grave," said Corporal Globe.

They thought I was dead and buried. And they even risked their lives to find my body. While careful, of course, to avoid undue familiarity I had throughout my Army career tried to be as democratic to my N.C.O.'s as my superior rank would permit, but I had not realized till then what depths of loyalty my efforts had tapped.

"I'm all right, chaps," I cried. "I'm over here in a cave."

"Oh! Good Gawd, no!" said Corporal Globe. "Not him!"

The poor chap thought he was hearing a ghost. I had many a good joke with him about it afterwards.

"I'm alive and kicking," I said. "But tied up. Rally on me! Quickly!"

They scrambled up into the cave and Sergeant Transom cut me loose.

"Thanks a lot, chaps," I said. "I'm deeply touched by your devotion. . . . But no time for talk, I'm afraid. We've got to get moving. The Arabs or a Boche patrol might be here at any moment."

"Who's that tied up over there?" asked the sergeant.

"That's my prisoner. He's a Boche masquerading as a Wog, just like I was. But I penetrated his disguise and he'd have been back in our lines already if those Arab brigands hadn't jumped me. But we'll take him up now. We'll have to carry him because he's still flat out."

"Right. Get him up, you three," said Sergeant Transom.

"But, Sarge," said Corporal Dooley. "What about the stuff? Ain't we going to . . ."

"Now we found the governor? Use your loaf, Dooley, and get that Jerry up on your shoulders."

Darkness came down as I led my non-commissioned cortège back through the *wadis* towards our lines. The corporals, two at the head and one at the heels, bore my captive up the broken slope of Djebel Tokurna, cursing their awkward burden in unison as they stumbled and stubbed their way among the uncertain rocks.

[91]

"How did you find out what happened to me?" I asked Sergeant Transom.

"There was a Wog kid saw them cop you. He came up and told us. We asked around and found there used to be a Wog cemetery for some peculiar sect down there. They were buried in the caves with all their worldly wealth in the coffins. The locals reckon a leading gang of grave robbers have buried a big cache of jewellery somewhere in the *wadis*."

"And the Arabs that attacked me thought I was after it."

"That's about it. But they were scared of cutting your throat when they found you were a British officer."

The stretcher party veered towards platoon headquarters as we came safely over the hill and down the reverse slope.

"Keep going, chaps," I said. "Straight back to Company headquarters. This may just be the identification they're waiting for back in Algiers. He may even be a high-ranking intelligence officer."

"His bloody brains weigh heavy if he is," said Corporal Hink. "I'm sweating cobblestones under this flannel nightshirt."

But they toiled manfully on over the extra three hundred yards back to the farmhouse.

"Good God Almighty!" exclaimed Major Arkdust as we lay down our burden in the scullery. "What the hell are you playing at? Ali Baba and the Forty Thieves?"

I saluted as smartly as my garments would allow.

"Goodbody reporting, sir, having returned from patrol under indigenous disguise. I have brought back this German prisoner whom I captured when he was attempting to reconnoitre our positions dressed as an Arab."

"Did you, by George! How did you spot him?"

"By his field boots, sir, protruding into view from under his burnous."

"Let's have a look at the beggar." He hitched up the gown and there were the telltale jackboots. "You've certainly got him trussed up. And laid out as well. Get him untied and we'll see if we can bring him round. . . . In the meantime, Sergeant Major, get on the blower and tell the I.O."

We unbound the German, cut away his wrappings and pulled off his boots for safety.

"He's dressed like a Wog all through," said the major, "and even his feet are brown."

"Damned thorough, the Boche, sir," I said. "A bit of a scrub with paraffin and we'll soon have the stain off."

Major Arkdust touched the crinkly, dark hair and pulled back an eyelid. Then he turned over the German's hands to reveal the pink-padded palm. He took a long, slow breath.

"You'll not be changing his colour with paraffin. Nor anything short of skinning. What you've got here, Goodbody, is not a German dressed as a Wog. It's a Wog dressed, as far as his feet are concerned, as a German. A plain, ordinary Wog who's won a pair of field boots from a dead Boche."

I had not, since being knocked out, seen my captive in a good light. My company commander was indubitably right. I saluted smartly. One can always, at least, be polite.

"A thousand apologies, sir. I have not previously had opportunity to examine the prisoner in detail owing to having been assaulted by grave robbers and . . ."

"By whom?"

"By Arab grave robbers, sir, who thought I was after their cache and prevented me . . ."

He waved his hand across my face for silence.

"My dear Goodbody, I just haven't got the time. I'm fighting the Germans. I'll leave the Arabs to you. That chap looks to me as if he's got concussion. So just be a good fellow and take him down to the M.O. And for God's sake get out of those blasted bed sheets."

I looked at my Bedouin corporals.

"It's only about five hundred yards," I said. "And most of it down hill."

Groaning like galley slaves, they picked up their patient and raised him limply to their shoulders.

"Gawd Strewth!" said Corporal Dooley as they maneuvered out through the scullery door. "Half the night up and down the Rocky Mountains, dressed up like the Sheikh of Araby, playing stretcher-bearer to a bloody Wog. If I'd have known about those grave robbers earlier, I'd have sent them down a free pardon and my own personal cutthroat."

Chapter Nine

... if all the genius of the world had united to plan the perfect operation, the operation would fail most dismally if the troops were deficient in fortitude. A plan, that is, is ultimately dependent upon the soldier's morale; and, other things being equal—or not grossly disparate —a battle is won by that side whose soldiers are prepared to deny their weariness, to maintain their purpose, and to go on fighting a little longer than the others ...

ERIC LINKLATER
The Campaign in Italy

THE TROOPS MUST be drawn up in a hollow square, the instruction commanded, and a small platform erected in the centre so that no soldier is within twenty yards of it.

It was one morning at the end of April 1943, that the Fourth Musketeers were thus drawn up on parade in a clearing of a cork forest near Beja. There was a flummery of top brass and then He strode along the hand-swept path and up on to the podium. He was a thin, ferret-faced little man, utterly lacking any of the beef, bull neck, and Poona-boom obligatory in the British High Command. His voice was rasping, high pitched, and dispassionate.

"I've come here today to have a talk with you. Break ranks and gather round me."

For a moment, we hesitated, our reflexes unwilling to obey an order so alien to all our training.

"Right," muttered the R.S.M. "Break ranks. Get on with it."

[95]

The formal lines swayed, bulged, and then burst as the parade of soldiers became a crowd of people and we swayed forward around the platform. With the breaking of the rigid pattern of drill formation all the tension flowed out of the occasion. That mental block which debars from the brain of a soldier comprehension of a brass hat's exhortation, was broken. At such military High Mass the minds of the congregation normally numb as their bodies stiffen to attention. The general speaks, but the soldier never gets the message.

"I've just come here today," He said, "to have a chat with you. We're going to have a bit of a party soon. Good party it's going to be, too. Really going to hit them for six this time. Right out of Africa, that's where Rommel's going this time. And I've come here to tell you how we're going to do it. But before I do that I want to say two things to you. First, that you have done a fine job here in this difficult country of Tunisia. And second, that I've heard what a fine show the Musketeers have put up. Very fine show, indeed. Absolutely first-class job. But then the Musketeers always do a first-class job, don't they?"

Chests began to swell a little all round.

"Now I want to tell you just how we're going to set about our last battle in Africa. We won't be having it for a few days yet because I'm not ready. . . . Never want to fight a battle till you're ready. That's the way to lose battles. And we're not here to lose, are we? We're here to win. That's our job. To win. And that's what I told the Prime Minister when he was here the other week. Very great man, of course, but a bit impatient, you know. It's high time, he said to me, that you had another battle. I can't have a battle yet, I said to him, I'm not ready. Why not? he said. Haven't got enough guns, tanks, or aeroplanes yet, I said. Never put my chaps into battle, sir, unless we've got at least twice as much stuff as the enemy. Never put my chaps into battle unless we're sure to win. And if we're going to be sure of winning this next party I want

[96]

five hundred guns, three hundred tanks and two hundred aeroplanes. And I'm not going to attack till I've got 'em."

His dry, matter-of-fact tones dealt with the hazards of war as simple arithmetic, listing its deadly requirements as undramatically as the weekend groceries.

"Well," He went on, sighing at such illogical behaviour, "the Prime Minister got a little cross with me. Told me in no uncertain terms, you know, he still wanted me to attack right away. And I had to be firm with him . . . quite firm . . . very sorry, sir, I said, but we can't have a battle until you give us those tanks and guns and aeroplanes. I'm afraid he was a bit difficult about it for a while . . . very tough chap, you know, when he's made up his mind . . . but in the end he came round to my point of view. And now he's sent us the stuff I wanted. We've got our five hundred guns, three hundred tanks and two hundred aeroplanes and we can have our party."

"Chuck in a couple of crates of Guinness," said Corporal Dooley, "and I'll be coming with you myself."

"And now I'll tell you my plan. It's a very simple one. Always pays to be simple. Get too complicated and you disperse your effort. And that's the way to lose battles. But we're going to win . . . that's what we're going to do . . . win. . . . So we shall attack at one point with everything we've got. Pick out, say, about three hundred yards of the enemy's line. Not too big, you know. Don't want to waste anything. And just before dawn we'll get those two hundred aeroplanes to come over all together and bomb the daylights out of that strip. Then we'll fire all those five hundred guns at once on the same place. As soon as they've finished we'll attack with two infantry divisions supported by two armoured divisions, punch straight through to Tunis and hit the Boche for six clean out of Africa. . . . That's what we're going to do. We're going to attack with overwhelming superiority and we're going to win. There's no doubt about that . . . no doubt

[97]

whatever. . . . Once we break through and get him off balance we've just got to keep at him . . . keep at him like a terrier after a rat . . ."

And He talked on, simply, prosaically, about the mechanics of the coming battle for another five minutes, reiterating His confidence of victory, wished everybody luck, demanded the support of Almighty God, left cartons of cigarettes for distribution and disappeared back down the forest path in His jeep.

"Blimey!" said Corporal Hink. "It's going to be a cakewalk. We can't lose."

"Poor old Jerry," said Private Clapper. "Two hundred bombers and five hundred guns. I'm glad I ain't up there."

"Little feller, wasn't he?" said Corporal Globe. "Looked more like a debt collector's clerk than a general. But he's got the right idea, ain't he? Three hundred tanks is a bit more like it. All we ever seen round here yet is Churchills getting knocked off by eighty-eights in little penny packets."

"Publicity," said Private Drogue. "That's all it is, mate. Selling war like other blokes sell soap. The old bull, that's what we just been getting. All in aid of getting everybody off across no-man's-land at the happy, laughing double."

"If you got to go," said Corporal Dooley, "you might as well go cheerful. All the brass hats ever came round us before spent their time bellyaching about you got your gas-cape rolled the wrong way, your blanco's the wrong colour, or there's a man in the front rank got a stud short on his left boot. But that bloke, now, he may not have been twopennorth of scrag-end to look at, but he sounds as though he's on the same side as us."

"Don't kid yourself," said Private Spool. "That's just the same old madam. Bash on, chaps. Rah-rah-rah. Gawd's on our side, you can't lose and my middle name's Napoleon."

I left the parade ground with fire smouldering in my belly, confident of victory in the coming battle; not only because His address had inspired me, but also because His analysis of

[98]

the situation, armament estimates, and general plan of campaign, agreed entirely with my own. Which was, perhaps, just as well, for a fortnight later the five hundred guns broke loose and the Musketeers came through the promised gap behind the tanks and went hightailing it for Tunis. C Company was in battalion reserve fifteen miles from Tunis when Major Arkdust sent for me.

"We've got a job," he said. "The tanks up to our north are running out of steam. They're having to harbour up for tonight and need infantry protection. C Company comes under command of 17th Dragoons and is to work with their Z Squadron. They are still trying to push on and, with the Boche holding in some places and pulling out in others, the situation is very fluid and the available information is confused. We have, however, the locations of each troop at midday, that's almost an hour ago now, and the axes on which they are advancing. Platoons will be allocated to locate and protect each tank troop as follows . . ."

Twelve Platoon's orders were to link up with Eight Troop of the Dragoons last heard of swinging west along a third-class road to Jaiba. We moved off in four scout trucks at two o'clock and drove across the newly sown battlefield. German traffic signs were still up, brewed-up tanks, Tigers, Churchills, Shermans, smouldered here and there in a last drift of smoke, the shell scars on shattered buildings were livid and unweathered, and the bodies about them not yet wearing their grey pall of dust. The going was fairly good on the main road where the sappers had been at work, but the craters and demolitions were still thick and virgin when we turned up the side road to Jaiba. The detours of the tanks were not always easy enough for our trucks and we had to stop and dig our way round some obstacles. Our progress was slow and the route tortuous. Map reading was difficult and there were many more sidetracks and junctions than we had on our map.

"Jerry must have had a supply depot or something round here," said Sergeant Transom. "There's new tracks running all ways and you can't pick out the old road at all. No wonder those tank boys couldn't give us a reference. The map's useless. We'll have to work off the compass."

"We don't need to," I said. "Jaiba is not our objective. It's the tanks we've got to locate."

"And how do we do that?"

"Follow their tracks." I pointed to the striped imprint which the tank tracks, mud-laden by the last detour, had left on the road. "We can forget the map and follow the footmarks. They pick up new mud at every loop."

My idea worked magnificently and we made far better time unhindered by map reading. We rolled steadily on for half an hour, the spoor winding clearly before us, freshened nicely at each piece of cross-country.

Our first setback came as we crossed a flat, rocky area where deviations were unnecessary and the caterpillars dried out, leaving no obvious impression. At a meeting of five ways we lost the scent completely. I debussed the platoon, spread them out shoulder to shoulder, eyes to the ground, and led them in controlled scrutiny like a row of hunchback grouse beaters.

"Pity we ain't got my brother Geronimo here," said Private Drogue.

"Why?" asked Private Spool.

"Because he's a Red Indian. Just the boy for finding armour-plated footprints. Give him half-a-bar and he'd bring his Comanche bloodhounds and smell out those petrol-footed dragoons."

This mass drive met no success whatever. It was not till I quartered the area personally that I finally detected the tank trail again on a sand-filled crack a hundred yards down the extreme right fork.

"I dunno," said Sergeant Transom, looking at the sun, "but I'd have thought they'd have been running more round towards the north."

Round the next bend, however, we came off the rock and

dropped into a river valley where the verges were soft and muddy and the Shermans had left their imprints deep and clear. Bogged down, one wheel axle deep off the edge of the macadam, stood a German light armoured car.

"They were going back in a hurry," I said. "It wouldn't have taken much to get that out."

"Unless the motor's gone phut," said Sergeant Transom. He climbed inside and poked around the controls. The engine whirred over, coughed once or twice and started like a bird.

"Let's take it with us," he said. "Never know when it might come in handy."

We dug the wheel out, shoved down a sand channel and got it back on the road. I put it in the middle of the column, under command of Corporal Dooley, so that the Dragoons would not see it first and mistake us for Jerries. The going along the river valley was first-class and there were no more demolitions. We made fine speed in the wake of the tanks and began coming out of the wild country and into the outskirts of a village.

"This might be Jaiba," I said.

"Wherever it is," said Sergeant Transom. "They're not over-pleased to see us."

Farms and houses were springing up on the roadside, all happily undamaged, but none of the people in the gardens or standing at the windows gave us so much as a welcoming wave. Suddenly the black track marks swung wide across the road and turned into the gate of a farmyard.

"Here they are," I said. "We're up with the Dragoons."

Halting the trucks against the high, stone wall I got down and walked up the garden path between the tank ruts. I knocked on the farmhouse door. It opened.

"Good afternoon . . ." I said.

A German soldier looked at me.

"*Was wurden Sie . . . Mein Gott!*" he shouted. "*Englander!*"

He slammed the door in my face and I heard the bolt go home.

"Jesus Christ!" gasped Sergeant Transom. "Jerries!" He pointed at the ruts. "Those are Tiger tracks you've been following!"

I do not recall my feet touching ground as we flew down the path and back into the truck.

"Get rolling," yelled Sergeant Transom. "And Dooley! Ditch that arc across the gate."

He lobbed three smoke bombs over the wall as Corporal Dooley ran the German armoured car across the entrance, and transferred to my truck. Machine gun fire came through the smoke and spat chips off the top of the wall as our column roared off down the hill, engines screaming flat out in second till we made the cover of the next bend. It was a sharp hairpin, and as we braked hard to get round it a civilian with a shotgun leapt on to my running board.

"Maquis!" he shouted. "Maquis . . . keep going. I show you safe place."

We raced out of the hairpin and the road skirted round a bluff. Suddenly, down below, we saw masses of houses, monumental buildings, and the blue of the sea.

"Where's this?" I yelled to our hitchhiker. "Jaiba?"

"Jaiba? You're miles past Jaiba. This is Tunis!"

"Tunis!" I cried. "Good Lord!"

"Tunis!" groaned Sergeant Transom. "And Tigers behind us."

"Tunis!" beefed Private Drogue. "I ain't transferred to no suicide squad."

"Tunis!" yelped Private Spool. "Stop the bus. We're going the wrong way."

"Tunis!" said Corporal Dooley. "Then I'll be asking the foreman for me cards."

"Turn left here!" snapped our guide. "Quickly . . . now right . . . and straight through the yard of that factory . . ."

We twisted and turned, up alleys barely wide enough for

[102]

the trucks, across vacant lots, along canal banks, through a railway tunnel and down into dockland. Swaying and rattling over the broken cobbles we swung through a warren of warehouses, over a slender steel bridge and on to a wharf. . . . The doors of a vast corrugated iron barn were open . . . the trucks roared inside and slammed to a frantic stop among serried ranks of grain bags.

The magnitude of our deed suddenly struck me.

"First into Tunis, Sergeant Transom," I said. "For the glory of the Musketeers."

"And first for the flaming firing squad when Jerry comes over that bridge."

"Not to have no fear," said the maquis-man. "I fix it. I am Henri Jardot. How do you do?"

He extended an old-world hand and I shook it on the run back to the entrance.

"Pleased to meet you. I am Lieutenant Goodbody."

We helped him slide shut the doors from outside and the vehicles were hidden. He turned to a winding gear at the head of the bridge and started cranking for all he was worth. . . . Slowly the carriageway pulled away from the mainland and swung towards us.

"It's a swing-bridge," said Sergeant Transom. "We're pulling up the ladder behind us."

We joined the panting winder and soon the bridge lay flat against our bank. Thirty yards of dark water separated us from the dock. We ran back inside the building.

"Is this an island?" said Sergeant Transom.

"Yes," said the Frenchman. "Very small. Just this warehouse and the wharf around it. All belongs to me."

"Corporal Dooley," ordered Sergeant Transom, pointing to the gallery which ran round the storehouse. "Get up there and lay a couple of Brens covering the bridge. We don't want Jerry nipping across and winding it back."

"Not to have no fear. No one can move the bridge without the handle." Henri held up the pinioned crank which he had

[103]

withdrawn from the wheelhouse. "The bridge turns only from this side."

He hung the handle from a peg near the door.

"That's a help, anyway," said the sergeant. "Corporal Hink . . . get a load of these sacks built up on the front walls. Corporal Globe, come down the back with me . . ."

With bastions of grain bags at strategic points and gun ports at every corner, I soon had the warehouse in a capital state of defence.

"I think," said Henri after half an hour had gone by with no interruption, "that the Boche lost our trail. Otherwise he would have been here by now."

"He might still be searching."

"Maybe. But I don't think so. I have men watching over there. The Boche has big trouble south of Tunis. Three— four divisions coming at him. He's not much time to worry about twenty—thirty men like you got up here in the north. He's still got thousands of men and knows all you can do is lie low till Tunis falls."

"If he's got all those troops round about," asked Sergeant Transom, "why did he let us get in so far?"

Henri's Dali moustache crinkled in admiration.

"That Boche armoured car. He thought, like we did, that coming back behind the Tigers you were a column of prisoners with armoured car escort. That's why we were all ready for you. We had ambush laid at the corner where I jumped you. . . . You damned brave man, Lieutenant, bluffing your way in like that with just twenty—thirty men. But you never stood no chance without tanks."

I shrugged with British devil-may-care.

"*Toujours l'audace,*" I said. "Nothing venture, nothing gain. What is life but a gamble with death?"

I was about to quote the pitch-and-toss bit from Montrose, when Corporal Dooley yelled down from the gallery.

"We got visitors. Ship, ahoy!"

Henri opened the wicket in the main door. Four rowing

[104]

boats were coming across from the mainland, loaded to the gunwales with women.

"Stop!" I cried. "Go back! This is a battle area. Out of bounds! W. D. property! Go back!"

I recognized their gaudy colours in a flash. An efficient officer can always learn something from his mistakes. I had profited from my unfortunate error at Cleptha. I could now recognize a prostitute when I saw one and here were four boatloads of them just making landfall on my fortress. Their vast, brassy haired captain, laocooned in beads, came at me like Hackenschmidt and folded me suffocating to her bosom.

"English!" she cried. "Always everybody love the English. We come when we hear. We give you big welcome and plenty good time."

"But, madame," I said, "we are in no position to . . ."

She held up a magisterial hand.

"You say not nothing. This is for free! For the first of the English in Tunis everything is for free. I give you cards and you tell all your friends that come later to go to Rosabella for plenty good time."

She plucked from the chimney of her cleavage a pack of glit-edged cards and dropped them into my hand. The whole of Twelve Platoon had deserted their posts and were engaged in helping Rosabella's handmaidens to disembark themselves and their basket cargo of food, drink, and gramophone records.

"You very lucky, Lieutenant," said Henri. "She bring you best bad women in all Tunis. Now the Germans are going, she look for new custom."

"Stop!" I commanded. "Put those women down. Drop them back in the boats. You cannot land here, madame. You must take your employees back to the mainland."

"Why you like that?" demanded Rosabella. "You ain't queer or something?"

"No. Not at all. I order you to leave this island. We are not here to play games. We are fighting the Germans."

"Why you be like that? Don't you wanna good time? If you send my girls away, you know what they do?"

"I am not in the least concerned . . ."

"If you send them back they go and tell Germans just where you are. Then they bring guns and blow you all to hell."

"Oh . . . I see. . . ." That was more than I could risk. And a plan was brewing in my mind which required peace till nightfall. "Then they will have to remain on the island. But in purdah. . . . Sergeant Transom . . . construct a Ladies Only enclosure with grain bags against the end wall. . . . Everyone back to his post!"

When the harem was marked off by a wall of sacks, I herded the protesting females inside. I made a chalk sign with "Out of Bounds to British Troops" on one side and "No Females Past This Point" on the other. I placed Private Clapper on guard at the entrance, feeling that his continued concern for Mrs. Clapper's fidelity might make him a trustworthy eunuch.

"Is not right," wailed Madame Rosabella. "We come long way to give first English plenty good time."

"Is not right, three ruddy bags full," said Private Drogue. "For all the under we ever get we might as well be in the Salvation Army. Look at that biddy in the blue sweater. I could lose me way in her lot."

I called together my order group.

"Since we have penetrated into the heart of the enemy's camp," I said, "it is our duty to exploit our success. As the general emphasized, we must keep at the enemy like a terrier after a rat. Also with the arrival of these fallen women it is advisable that we leave the island before they upset the rank and file."

"Never mind the rank and file," muttered Corporal Dooley. "There's meself encumbered with two-bobs'-worth of Blackpool rock."

"The crucial battle for Tunis is being fought to the south.

A surprise attack on the Boche headquarters at this crucial moment would have a devastating effect. Henri can lead us to the building. We will therefore open the bridge at first dark and make a lightning raid on General von Arnim's headquarters."

There was a silence. They were clearly stunned by the brilliance of my plan.

"Do you mean, sir," said Sergeant Transom, "that we should go swanning down Tunis High Street in British trucks and have it out with General von Arnim personally with just one platoon?"

"Speed, Sergeant, is an essential element of surprise."

He turned to Henri.

"How far away is the Boche headquarters?"

"About two—three miles."

"And how far d'you reckon we'd get?"

"Maybe half mile, if we have luck. Then just guns, tanks and roadblocks all the way. You ain't just brave man, Lieutenant. You maybe crazy."

"We don't want to be no Charge of the Light Bridge, sir," said Corporal Hink. "I don't care if nobody never writes no poetry about me."

"I ain't after the V. C., sir," said Corporal Globe. "Specially not posthumously."

"You'll be needing, of course, sir," said Corporal Dooley, "the senior corporal to stay behind and look after the billets."

I stressed to them again the vital military advantage of surprise and while I was talking I noticed the attention of my order group wandering continually towards the Ladies' Enclosure, where three of the most nubile occupants were belly dancing to "Ramona" on the gramophone. I detected then, of course, that their objections to my plan of attack were founded not on valid tactical considerations, but on simple lechery. They were merely being obstructive because they wished to stay on the island with the loose women. This strengthened my determination to carry through my plan and I gave orders then and there for a departure rehearsal.

"We must first lay on a drill for opening the bridge. Get the winding handle, Corporal Hink."

"I can't, sir. It's gone."

The peg on the wall was empty. Private Drogue spoke up from his post near by.

"I think it was one of them women nicked it while you were talking, sir. It might have been that bride in the blue sweater with top-heavy torso." He growled like a frustrated gorilla. "Shall I search her for you, sir?"

There was a sudden splash in the water outside.

"That's it, sir," shouted Private Spool from the gallery. "That's the handle gone in the drink. Looked like a tart slinging it, too."

"Well," said Sergeant Transom, beaming happily. "We can't get the bridge over now. So we can't go hell-for-leather after von Arnim, can we?"

"We will proceed on foot," I said decisively. "That way we can avoid all roadblocks. And we will cross over in the prostitutes' punts."

I went to the powder-room and told Madame Rosabella that I held her responsible for the loss of the winding handle. If the culprit was not produced, she herself would be tried by drumhead court-martial for obstructing an officer of the British Army in the due performance of his duty.

"But why you so mean-hearted?" she demanded. "Why you want to take English boys away from here? Plenty food, plenty drink, plenty good time for everybody. You don't find no better girls down there in Tunis. Why you so spiteful to me?"

I went out with Sergeant Transom through the wicket door. The corporals were out there already. Dooley was kneeling on the edge and thrashing the water with a plank.

"If only we'd been a minute earlier, sir," he panted, "we'd

[108]

have cotched them at it. It was the women that cut them loose and we just saw the skirts of them go flickering round the corner."

The four boats were drifting fifty yards off and making all speed away from the mainland.

"This is deliberate sabotage," I snapped. "Men have faced the firing squad for less."

I marched straight back into the shed and put Madame Rosabella under close arrest. Corporal Dooley suggested I should have all the women searched for scissors, but I deemed it unwise to allow any opportunity for incidental lechery.

"No bridge, no boats, sir," said Sergeant Transom cheerfully. "Looks like we're here for the night."

"We can swim across."

"Half of them are non-swimmers."

"Then half can swim and half can come across on a line."

"What about the guns? And our clothes. We going to attack General von Arnim mother-naked?"

"Our clothes can be towed over in a truck canopy. There's a way of making it waterproof. I have the plan in my O. C. T. U. notes on River Crossings."

"If you make English boys take off their clothes for swim," screamed the furious Rosabella, "I tell my girls throw all clothes in the river."

"If any of the lads take their trousers off, sir," said Corporal Hink, "them floozies'll go raving mad."

"Disrobing may not be necessary," I said. "The water may be shallow enough to wade through. I will make a reconnaissance. If it is wadeable I will take a line across myself."

It was just falling first dark as I took off my jacket, shoes and socks, rolled up my trouser legs and lowered my foot down the side of the wharf and into the thick water. I would have taken off my trousers, but for all those women in the shed. Not, mark you, that in my case Corporal Hink's remark was in any way applicable. I am not, thank God and a Methodist upbringing, that sort of chap. I had the line tied to my belt to leave my hands free. . . . I stretched my leg deeper and deeper, feeling for the bottom, and rolled my body as far as I could towards the edge . . .

For lack of eyewitness evidence to that effect, I will not formally say that someone pushed me—after all I was surrounded by my own trusted N. C. O.'s and Sergeant Transom himself was holding the line. Whether I felt a toe prise my buttock or whether I rolled over a stone on the wharf I do not know, but I suddenly found myself falling over the edge and floundering in the water. . . . I sank deep into the oily depths but never touched bottom . . . treading water against the drag of my clothing . . . dog-paddled with an overhead action, I fought my way gasping to the surface and turned on my back.

"Hold on, sir," shouted Sergeant Transom, "I'll soon lug you in."

In retrospect, I take pride that even at this sudden turn of events I kept my head. Military training stood by me and I made a quick adjustment to my original wading plan.

"Pay out the rope," I cried, "I will swim across now and establish a line for the non-swimmers."

I struck out with my powerful side-trudgeon and bore steadily across the gap. When I had made ten yards from the island the doors of the shed slid open and Madame Rosabella and her troop of harpies came screeching out.

"Stop!" they cried in various tongues. "Come back! Do not steal the English boys. . . . Traitor! Saboteur! Vile enemy of hard-working girls!"

They hurled at me bottles, driftwood, and old shoes, and as I turned on my back to reason with them, the barrel-chested blueshirt who had taken Drogue's fancy heaved up a bag of grain and hurled it over the water.

"Ladies!" I said. "Ladies! Desist!"

The sky was blacked out by the bottom of a grain bag . . . it landed squarely on my face and I went down into dark-green oblivion with canal juice gurgling acrid in my lungs.

I recovered consciousness three hours later, warm and drowsy, with hot air blowing across my flattened face. A petrol cooker was roaring, candles flickering and my clothes were hanging on a line. I was lying under blankets on a bed of sacks and Madame Rosabella was smoothing my brow.

"He's all right," said Sergeant Transom. "Here you are, sir. Drink this."

Dazed and half-awake, I drank from the glass and some electric liquid coursed vividly down my throat.

"What is it?" I asked.

"Brandy. Medicinal brandy, of course. It's what the doc would give you if he was here. Have some more."

It certainly made me feel better, so I drained the rest of the glassful and found myself sinking comfortably back to sleep. That grain bag must have hit me pretty hard because my memories of that night have always been very disjointed. I remember waking up a couple of times to hear soft music playing, bottles clinking, and rosy figures dancing a Greek bacchanal. Once I thought I saw Private Drogue losing his way in the lot of his female shot-putter. I couldn't be sure it was Drogue, however, because his face was buried in the vast white billows of her bosom which, with the massage of a masterbaker, he was kneading up over his ears.

When I woke in daylight, my head was beating bass drums and my mouth was like the bottom of a bird cage. The girls and all their trappings were gone.

"Henri found us a boat and I got rid of them at first light," said Sergeant Transom. "After what they done to you, sir, the boys didn't want them hanging round here no more. There's been a hell of a barney down in the town and I reckon the Jerries have packed in. Henri's gone down to check up and see if he can hear anything about the Musketeers."

"Good," I said. "Then we must get moving on to the mainland right away."

"Afraid we can't, sir. You remember one of them tarts slung the bridge handle in the drink? We've tried all ways to work the wheel, but it won't move without it."

"Then we must find the handle."

"What, down there?" He pointed into the sludge water. "We don't even know where to start looking."

"A little logical thought will narrow down the area of search. We know approximately where Private Spool saw the woman when she threw the handle. We can estimate the distance that an average woman could throw an object of that weight. If we then methodically search in that radius we should locate the handle."

"But supposing it was that biddy who copped you with the sack. If she tossed it, that handle could be anywhere between here and Tunis Town Hall."

In spite of the anvils clanging behind my eyes I made the necessary calculations, paraded the eighteen swimmers in the party, stripped to their underpants, and led them into the water. Unfortunately all my N. C. O.'s turned out to be non-swimmers, and I had to paddle around the critical semicircle myself and ensure that each man was stationed correctly.

"Now," I cried, when I had all eighteen treading water in the proper area. "On the command 'Dive,' each man will descend to the bottom, search in a six-foot circle and return to the surface. We will then close in the arc to one yard nearer the island and repeat the drill until the handle is found. . . . Ready, men? Prepare to dive!"

A motor horn blasted from the mainland.

"What in God's name are you doing in there, Goodbody?" yelled Major Arkdust. "Holding a blasted swimming gala?"

"We're the Luton Ladies' Formation Team," said my batman, Private Gripweed. "Imitating bloody water lilies."

"No, sir," I cried. "We are taking steps to open this swingbridge so that we may leave the island. I have pleasure to

[112]

report, sir, that the Musketeers were first into Tunis. Primus in Tunis, sir, as one might say. We got here at 16.29 hours yesterday."

By treading water at double-time—an aquatic trick I had learnt in the Kettering Municipal Swimming Baths and Washhouse—I kept myself waist-high out of the water and held my right hand, from the words "Primus in Tunis," rigidly at the salute.

"If you got this far at four o'clock, why the hell are you still on that island?"

"We were besieged, sir, all night."

"Who by?"

"Women, sir."

"By women?"

"Yes, sir. Loose women, sir, as a matter of fact. Fancy ladies, if you know what I mean. They wanted to keep us here for business purposes. They cut the boats adrift and threw the bridge winding handle in the water. We are now searching systematically for that handle . . ."

Henri was talking excitedly to my commander and pointing across the bridge.

"What's that sticking out of the side of the wheelhouse?" yelled Major Arkdust. "He says that's the blasted handle."

I looked where he bade me. The handle, polished and bone dry was in place and ready for winding. Someone had put it back while I was arranging my frogmen.

There was only one course open to me. I stopped my doublequick paddling, set my legs rigidly together and, still at the salute, allowed myself to descend slowly into the concealing depths of the bottle-green sea. As I went down like a captain without a bridge I saw Sergeant Transom backing Privates Drogue and Spool up against the wheelhouse and thrashing them about their heads with my K. D. trousers.

[113]

Chapter Ten

Commanders in all grades must have qualities of leadership; they must
have initiative; they must have the "drive" to get things done. . . .
Above all, they must have that moral courage, that resolution, and that
determination which will enable them to stand firm when the issue
hangs in the balance. Probably one of the greatest assets a commander
can have is the ability to radiate confidence in the plan and operations
even (perhaps especially) when inwardly he is not too sure about the
outcome . . . you must watch your own morale carefully . . . if your
heart begins to fail you when the issue hangs in the balance, your
opponent will probably win . . .

F.-M. Viscount Montgomery of Alamein
Memoirs

After i had taken Tunis, the regiment settled down at
Kalougie to rest and refit. Encamped in an olive grove above
a sapphire bay, we could have seen out the war from that site.
We were regarded as God's gift by the local Chamber of
Trade and hordes of Arabs descended upon us daily selling
fish, fruit, eggs, and young women. To protect ourselves from
our commercial allies we had to post more sentries and fix
more barbed wire than had served to keep us safe from the
Germans.

Captain Tablet called me to him one day in July 1943.

"I have a special job for you, Goodbody. The All-Highest
have decided, at last, that our daily invasion of Wogs must be
brought under hygenic control. Each unit is to appoint a
Civil Liaison Officer to carry out this function. With your

company commander's approval, you have been selected as C. L. O. of this camp. Full details of your duties are contained in this folder. Briefly, you must form a nominal roll of security-cleared and medically accepted Arabs and control the issue of passes so that only forty per days are allowed entry to the camp. You are authorized to appoint your own interpreter at Class IV rate of pay and a jeep will be provided by the M. T. O. for your use during the first fortnight."

I was most gratified at this mark of the adjutant's confidence in me. I had been worried that he might still be bearing malice from the Juniper court-martial.

"You may rely, sir, that I will control these civilians to the utmost of my ability. After all," I chuckled jocularly, "I was a civilian myself once."

"A fact," he said thinly, "which you give the Army little opportunity to forget."

I was almost out of the tent when he called me back.

"Just a moment, Goodbody. There is something else for the C. L. O."

I returned to attention before his desk. He opened a file and smiled blissfully at its contents.

"This is a special instruction on medical clearance. They are particularly worried at Army level about the outbreaks of dysentery and believe that they are spread by Arab carriers. No pass may be issued to a trader until he had been cleared of this suspicion by analysis of a sample of his excrement."

He placed on the desk a small cylindrical tin and beamed at it in vast content.

"I recall from your lectures on porcyliocosis how knowledgeable you are in medical matters and know that you will enjoy persuading each of our one hundred and fifty Wog friends to fill one of these charming little tins with his personal contribution, so that you may attach a form MDS 7004 in quadruplicate stating the name, age, address, and occupation of the donor at Part I and your certification as Part II

[115]

that you verified by personal inquiry that the sample did issue only from the above mentioned."

"You mean, sir," I said, "that I've got to ask each of those Arabs for a tinful of . . . a tinful of . . ."

"Exactly, my dear chap. And a very sanitary service you will be doing us all."

I went down into Kalougie and fixed myself up with an interpreter, Class IV. His name was Bubilya and he had learnt his Class IV English on an American tanker. He had one eye and wore a yellow baseball sweater and a pair of postman's trousers. I gave him as badge of office a steel helmet with C. L. O. (Int.) painted on it. When I unpacked the crate of tins and explained to him our first assignment, he asked for a week's money in advance.

"Jeez, boss!" he said, "I never heard nobody wanting to collect that goddammed stuff before. What the hell your general going to do with it?"

"Analyse it."

"Come again, boss."

"Analyse it. Break it down into tiny pieces so that he can tell what it's made of."

He was amazed.

"But everybody knows what it's made of. It's just plain . . ."

"That's all it may be to unscientific minds like yours, Bubilya. But to the Director of Medical Services it is chock full of fascinating information."

He looked wonderingly into the depths of a tin, shrugged helplessly and got on with the unpacking. The minds of the British were impenetrable.

On Saturday morning he got all hundred and fifty of the traders on parade. I had covered a table with the Union Jack and the glinting cylinders were ranged along it. I put on Service dress for the occasion. There is nothing like a bit of pomp to impress the natives.

"Tell them, Bubilya," I said, "that I bring them greetings from the Great White Father Across the Water."

"Come again, boss. They ain't Red Indians. They god-dammed Arabs."

"Tell them, then, that the Civil Liaison Officer sends them greetings and desires that each of them shall bring me his sample in one of those tins."

The proposition apparently took a lot of Arabic and Bubilya harangued them for a dramatic five minutes. He handed out the tins and they looked at them for a long time in bewildered silence. Then a hubbub of Arabian doubt beat up as each turned to the other for confirmation of his own ears. A plum pedlar, half hidden behind three feet of beard, tossed his can glittering up in the air, caught it, gestured at me and made a highly aspirated remark. A chuckle of appreciation rewarded him and suddenly the whole crowd burst in a wild gale of laughter, all hands pointing my way and hichoccing in delight.

"What are they saying, Bubilya?"

"Everybody say you very funny man. They say you please go on with next funny joke. They not had good laugh like you in Kalougie since muezzin fell off minaret."

"Tell them," I said, putting on my fiercest military expression, "that I am quite serious and that no one will be allowed to trade in the camp unless he has given me his . . . his personal contribution."

They hung on Bubilya's words as if he were Bob Hope and dissolved in fresh peals of hilarity when he finished.

"They say, boss, you ought to be on Radio Tunis. They say they give you money to let them come into camp. That all O. K. But they not give you lumps of that goddammed stuff. They got respect for British officer. Worst insult you can pay a man round Kalougie is to go to post office and send him packet of that goddammed stuff."

"Persist, Bubilya. Convince them that I am serious. Demonstrate to them the simplicity of my request."

When he took a tin and demonstrated, they went lunatic with laughter, stamping around hysterically, leaning on each other for support and collapsing in pairs to the ground when mirth became too much. The racket brought half the population of Kalougie to the fence in curiosity. A seventeen-stone, semitic monster tottered forward to ask advice of Bubilya.

"This man, boss, he say he got big problem. He say tin too small. He very big man. How the hell, he say, you expect him to balance on tiny tin like that?"

"You have clearly failed to communicate my requirements, Bubilya. Demonstrate again."

While he went into his encore, the adjutant came up.

"Don't let me interrupt you, my dear chap," he said. "Just carry on with the good work."

He settled himself under an olive tree to watch. A confabulation of four elders talked earnestly to Bubilya.

"These very wise men, boss, they worried about you. They say you don't do yourself no good collecting up all this god-dammed stuff in cigarette tins. It not natural for grown man. They say you do better for yourself if you collect stamps or beads or funny-shaped stones . . . anything but this god-dammed stuff."

A wild-eyed dervish came raving angrily out of the crowd. Bubilya ran behind me for protection.

"This man very angry, boss. He not bright in the head. He say you insult him, you spit on his manhood. He say little tin like that all right for child or small weak woman, but no good for him. He could fill twenty tins like that, no trouble at all, maybe more . . ."

The four elders dragged the wild one back on to parade and Captain Tablet smiled seraphically in the shade of his tree. Colonel Plaster and Major Arkdust were coming towards me from the orderly room. My reputation for leadership and discipline was at stake. My business training stood me in good stead and inspiration hit me happily. Everything has a price to an Arab; he would sell his own mother for ready money.

[118]

"Silence!" I yelled, crashing my stick on the table. The giggle and hubble-bubble died away.

"Tell them, Bubilya," I commanded, "that I will pay twenty francs to every one of them who comes to the camp gates at eight o'clock on Monday morning and brings me the required personal sample. Until then they must all leave the camp. And the offer will be withdrawn from anyone who is not outside the fence within two minutes flat."

At that rate, the lot would cost me about three pounds. It would be cheap at the price.

And the scent of money worked the oracle. They all jumped once in the air, crotched up their burnouses and flap footed through the gates and back to Kalougie. Their towns-folk ran beside them whooping in financial excitement. I saluted smartly as the colonel came by and I could see, as he wiped the dust of their passing from his eyebrows, that he was clearly impressed by the instant obedience of the natives to my authority. Captain Tablet went back to his office, disappointment darkening the lantern of his jaws.

"Dammed shop-keeper's mentality," he muttered. "Tradesmen's outlook. Put a price on anything. Even a handful of . . ."

It was my invariable practice during the war, and one which I can commend from experience to any young officer, to confirm verbal orders in writing at the earliest opportunity. Had I not given Sergeant Transom a written summary of my beach-landing plan, Twelve Platoon would never have taken Cleptha in time in my temporary absence. The spoken order, particularly when passed through an interpreter trained linguistically on an American tanker, to a collection of Arabs of indeterminate dialects may be misunderstood or forgotten. Put it in writing and it's there for all to see and remember. Also if you keep a copy in file you can always produce it as evidence of your own innocence at your subordinate's court-martial.

[119]

"To make sure, Bubilya, that everybody is quite clear about my requirements, you must write out a notice in Arabic and get the mayor to post it on the corporation noticeboard."

Our efforts were rewarded on Monday morning by overwhelming success. There was a queue a quarter of a mile long at the camp gates, men, women, and children, hundreds of them, the whole Arab population of Kalougie, each holding on high a little round tin and bellowing for twenty francs backsheesh. As I came into their view a happy cry of welcome went up.

"Himal-el-kebrouti! . . . Himal-el-kebrouti!"

"What are they shouting, Bubilya?"

"You famous man now, boss. That's their name for you. Himal-el-kebrouti."

"What does it mean?"

"It means, boss, the Rich Man Who Saves That Which All the World Throws Away."

"Why are there so many of them? There must be a couple of thousand or more."

Babilya jabbered through the wire at the front rank.

"They say yesterday you say everybody who brings personal sample gets twenty francs. You don't say only Arabs that trade in camp."

"But what about your notice? Wasn't that clear enough?"

He shrugged apologetically.

"I don't know for sure, boss. I don't write so good. Goddammed difficult writing in Arabic. They say notice say everybody, too."

"But where did they get all those tins?"

"Very smart blacksmiths in Kalougie, boss. Been working all over weekend making tins at two francs each. Everybody reckon they on eighteen francs profit."

Someone opened the gate. I couldn't be sure but it looked like Captain Tablet. The brown, tin-bearing sea burst inwards with a great cry of triumph.

"Himal! . . . Himal-el-kebrouti!"

Bubilya and I turned and ran for it. The regiment was just formed up on morning parade and the direct line to our jeep lay between the colonel and his command.

"Begging your pardon, sir," I shouted, saluting as best I could and giving him a placatory eyes-right as we shot by. Our multitude of anxious customers came swarming through the regimental ranks and the place looked like a miniature Fall of Khartoum. We made the jeep and my start would have taken medals at Le Mans. As we rolled away, the leading sample-seller latched on to the hood and Bubilya had to beat him off with his official helmet.

I had to drive right round the square to get back to the gate and when they saw my intent, the whole body about-turned and tore back to cut me off, bursting, *en route,* once more through the recovering ranks of the Commanding Officer's Parade. We scraped through inches before the rearguard could do a Gandhi on us, and I headed like a mechanized Arabian pied piper for Kalougie Town Hall. I made a lightning appreciation of the situation and gave out my orders as we switchbacked over the potholes.

"First, Bubilya, you must take down that notice. Second, the mayor will address the people explaining our requirements. Third, you must get a qualified scribe to write out a new notice. Any questions?"

"Yes, boss. Can't you go no faster? They're catching us up on goddammed mules."

I gave it all I could on the corrugated surface and we swung into the municipal yard with a good furlong lead over the enemy cavalry. Bubilya yelled the alarm and the burnoused beadles slammed shut the gates behind us. Panic, I could see, was about to set in, so I deliberately took my time alighting from the jeep. A leader of men must inspire by example, soothing with sangfroid the hysterics of his subordinates. I applied at Kalougie a trick which I used throughout my Army career to keep a cool top-knot in tight corners. As I walked slowly across the forecourt, I recited appropriate passages from Rudyard Kipling's *If*. The baying crowd swept up to the gate and I had just got to "If you can keep your head when all about you are losing theirs and blaming it on you," when someone threw his personal sample and hit me painfully under the right ear. Up went the clarion cry . . . "Himal-el-kebrouti!" . . . and I was forced to run the last five yards to cover as a hail of little tins came twinkling over the wall and burst fragrantly about me.

The mayor was quite useless. If I had been a Kalougian I would certainly not have voted for him at the next election. He would not obey my orders to address his townsfolk from the balcony and ran up and down his parlour wringing his pudgy, grocer's palms and squeaking fearfully. When the gates came down under the pressure of customers he dived under his desk and I was forced to take command. Fortunately, I remembered my O.C.T.U. legal training and the necessity for martial law to be declared before the Army could take over from the local authorities.

"Mr. Mayor," I said, kneeling down to find his ear beside the wastepaper basket, "I hereby proclaim martial law in Kalougie. As the senior officer present I am taking responsibility for the restoration of law and order."

The clerks were barricading the doors with furniture as a thousand fists beat on them outside.

"Stop that," I commanded crisply. "We will make a strategic withdrawal out through the back door."

"We won't, boss," said Bubilya. "There's more of them out back than up front."

We were surrounded. It was a time for quick decision.

"Withdrawal orders cancelled," I snapped. "Start in barricading the doors with furniture."

From the top back window we could see out across the coastal plain and up to the mountains. Black columns of people were descending on Kalougie from all directions. Half

Tunisia was on the move. As they came from the cover of the hills, the sun flashed on the little round tin each pilgrim was bearing reverently before him and the winding caravans shimmered like vast, chromium-plated snakes.

"Great Scott! Bubilya," I said. "Where on earth are they all coming from?"

"From the villages, Lieutenant," said a globular man in an off-white suit. "Word of your remarkable offer has spread through the district like wild fire. . . . The like of Himal-el-kebrouti has never passed this way before. May I have your confirmation, sir, that the Allied Forces have declared martial law in Kalougie?"

"Who is this man, Bubilya?"

"He newspaper man, boss, from *Tunis Express*. He come special for news about Himal-el-kebrouti."

A military man cannot be too careful in dealing with the Press. Look at all the trouble Montgomery had with them. I decided, for the time being, that a security blackout would be safest.

"Having been forced by circumstances to take over the maintenance of law and order from the civil authorities, I must temporarily prohibit the publication of any information likely to . . ."

An Arab face appeared suddenly at our second floor window and a fist bearing a tin came shattering through the glass.

"Mahmoud Abassa, chief," croaked the face. "Me not lousy bastard. Twenty francs, sir, thank you so much."

He had climbed up a pole leaned against the windowsill and swayed perilously from side to side as his competitors fought to mount beneath him. A dozen other poles came rearing out of the crowd.

"All hands on deck to repel boarders," I cried.

They were bringing the poles up from the docks in relays and as fast as we hurled them back from one window, they

[123]

spiked up at another. The windows below were all barred and shuttered and, so far, had defied the attacks of the lower-level brigades.

When I got out the fire hoses and beat them back with heavy water, my customers finally decided they were being welshed. Their baying lost its ingratiating, huckster note and roared now with cheated anger and hunger for revenge. They turned their poles as battering rams on the ground floor defences and began hurling fusillades of little tins through our broken windows. The hail of canned samples bruised down upon us like cannonballs.

"Everybody take cover," I commanded, "and be ready to counterattack when the bombardment lifts."

I dived under the desk where the mayor had fallen fast asleep. The reporter was already there talking on the telephone. I took it from him.

"You are under arrest, my man," I snapped. "Charged with breach of security instructions."

There was a thunderous crash and the Bastille fell down below.

"They're through, boss," quaked Bubilya, "and working their way up the goddammed stairs."

"To the roof!" I cried.

"They're up there already."

I made a rapid appreciation of the situation.

"Reinforcements," I said. "We must have reinforcements."

After five minutes' wrestling with the telephone I managed to get through to the regiment. Captain Tablet answered.

"Goodbody reporting, sir. We are beleagured by a large force of Arab civilians in Kalougie Town Hall, map reference 874912. Please send reinforcements."

"C Company is already on the way. To be followed by the colonel as soon as he can get off the line from the Corps Commander demanding why the hell he's declared martial law in Kalougie."

[124]

"The Corps Commander? How does he know?"

"The *Tunis Express* told him. What have you been doing? Holding a Press conference?"

"No, sir. I can explain everything. There is a reporter here in my garrison. But it's all right. I've put him under arrest . . ."

"And you'll be joining him, cocky, unless the bedouins get you before the colonel arrives."

And he hung up.

The mob was on the second floor now and hammering at our door with what sounded like the butt ends of spears. Overhead, angry men were battering through the roof. The floor was ankle-deep in little tins and dark faces were gibbering at every window. I drew my revolver and broke it to count the rounds.

"What's that for," asked the reporter, "Hari-kari?"

"Bubilya," I said, "is there a woman in the house?"

"A woman, boss," he said incredulously. "You want a woman? Now? This ain't no time, boss. And besides, there's no room under this desk."

"There are two women," said the reporter. "They've locked themselves in the stationery store. Why do you want to know?"

"For military purposes," I said tartly. "In order to allocate the proper reserve of ammunition. It is the custom in the British Army when surrounded by hostile natives to keep the last rounds for the women."

"Why?"

"To save them from a fate worse than death."

He watched slyly as I feverishly searched my pouch and pockets.

"But your gun's empty. You've got no ammunition."

"That is none of your business. It is due to gross inefficiency which I will take up with my batman later."

"You won't be able to shoot the women then, will you? You'll just have to stone them to death with your little tins."

"I have stood just about enough of your impudence, my man, and warn you that—"

The door came splintering in and a cascade of Arabs shot through, wailing and whooping around the office, hopping and hobbling painfully over the roller-bearing floor, scattering all ways to escape from the flailing pickaxe handles of Sergeant Transom, Privates Drogue, Spool, Clapper, and the rest of my trusty Twelve Platoon.

I came out from under the desk.

"Well done, Twelve Platoon," I said. "I knew you'd hasten to my succour."

"Gawd stone the crows!" said Private Drogue." We might have known it'd be him. Can't even be trusted to collect half-hundredweight of Arab . . ."

"Shut up," said Sergeant Transom. "You four go up and get them Wogs off the roof. Rest of you clear the yard and strew it with tin tacks . . ."

With the platoon under my command, I quickly got the situation in hand and all was quiet by the time the colonel's car appeared in the distance. I moved towards my jeep.

"Carry on, now, Sergeant. I'll meet the colonel and explain everything before he gets here."

"For Gawd's sake, sir, don't you do that. Give him an hour or two to cool down. . . . Take over, Corporal Dooley. Tell the major we're off chasing 'em back to the hills."

He joined me in the jeep and took over the wheel.

"But I'm sure, Sergeant, the colonel would understand if I explained things to him face to face."

"If he meets you face to face, he'll likely draw his six-gun and shoot you down. . . . And that wouldn't even be a fair fight, neither."

"Why not?"

"Because he's got ammunition."

And he let in the clutch and we roared away across the plain. I've often wondered since just how he knew that I had no ammunition, but I forgot to ask him at the time. It just shows, I suppose, how mutual understanding can be developed almost to the point of telepathy between an experienced officer and the right type of N.C.O.

Chapter Eleven

... In view of the existing situation in Italy ... you are empowered to make recommendations from time to time to lighten the provisions of the military armistice in order to enable the Italians, within the limits of their capacities, to wage war against Germany. ... You will encourage in all practicable ways the vigorous use, under your direction, of the Italian Armed Forces against Germany.

DIRECTIVE FROM PRESIDENT ROOSEVELT AND PRIME MINISTER CHURCHILL
TO THE SUPREME COMMANDER, MEDITERRANEAN

IT RARELY STOPPED RAINING in Italy. Naples was bathed in pale, winter drizzle when the Fourth Musketeers came ashore across the whale bellies of dead ships, and sleet laced down the wind as we trundled up the line to the Garigliano. The sky was Manchester grey behind Monte Cassino and clouds beetled down on the Abbey.

Major Arkdust came gloomily back from headquarters and called an order group.

"We are to take over part of the river line from the Guards," he said; "so that they can regroup for another go at Cassino. Our role is purely defensive and we'll be very thin on the ground. To fill in the holes we are to be assisted by the Italian Navy."

"But, sir," I asked crisply, "according to Baedeker, the Garigliano is not navigable beyond Forzando. How will the Navy get up here?"

"On foot."

The Italian Navy, he explained, had surrendered in September 1943. Their ships tied up for the duration, volunteers from among the sailors had been trained as infantry and formed into Liberation Groups.

"For political reasons," went on the major, "the Government is anxious that Italian soldiers, even though they be, in fact, dismounted mariners, shall early be seen in active combat on our side. Eighth Army Headquarters, however, have ordered that our amphibious allies should merely fill by their physical presence the most peaceful positions and be prevented at all costs from complicating our private battle with the Boche. So delicate an exercise in the art of war can only be entrusted to an experienced officer and I am, therefore, placing our Solferino Liberation Group of two hundred Italian foot-sailors under command of our senior subaltern, Lieutenant Goodbody."

"Thank you, sir," I said with deliberate modesty, careful not to look at my fellow platoon commanders lest they thought I was gloating.

It was my largest military responsibility to date. A thousand yards of the Garigliano to defend and, with good old Twelve Platoon, two hundred and forty men at my command. I took Sergeant Transom up on reconnaissance that night. It was four rocky miles from the road to my sector. The track would have quailed goats. It defeated jeeps and everything that couldn't be carried by man went up on reluctant mules. The ankle-deep mud was bent on swallowing our boots, but we fought our way up and patrolled my front. The river ran in a deep gorge, the banks steep and rough, in some parts precipitous. Sergeant Transom hung on a scrub oak and leaned out over the drop.

"The Colorado-bleeding-Canyon," he said. "Must be two hundred feet down to the river. Sheer as icebergs, too. Eagles'd go barmy laying eggs on that lot. No Jerry in his right mind is going to come climbing up there."

[129]

"This is just the sort of place for a surprise attack, Sergeant. No obstacle is insurmountable to determined troops. Think of the Maginot Line. Remember Wolfe at Quebec."

"I'll do my best, sir. But I'll lay even money if old Wolfe was down there, it'd be muffle up the rowlocks, boys, and back to the ship."

Captain Demoli, officer commanding the Solferino, came up next day. He was a round, puff-ball of a man, dark-jowled, voluble, and acutely conscious of his country's ignominy. He wore a pearl-handled automatic slung cowboy fashion on his hip and his face sweated, visibly, unceasingly.

"I come, *tenente*," he said, "to fight alongasida you for the *gloria d' Italia*. My men come from the sea to wash with their lifebloods the dirts from the face of Italia."

I welcomed him in the name of the British people to our happy band of Gallant Allies, explained that we were not anxious for any blood-letting at the moment and asked of his men only that they rest tranquil but alert.

"Have no fright, *tenente*," he cried, crouching like an indomitable Rigoletto. "They shall not pass. Not one centimetre of our sacred soil shalla we surrender to the *Tedeschi*. We die but we never retreat. Our bodies will lie down in death beside our gallant Inglesi cobelligerents."

"Thank you very much, *mon Capitan*," I said politely.

We were due to take over from the Guards at 22.00 hours the following night. The rendezvous with our Italians was fixed for 21.00 hours in a valley at the top of the track, two hundred yards back from the line. I waited there at the appointed time with Captain Demoli, Sergeant Transom, and the guides. The moon was hidden by clouds and it was raining stairrods. The skipper wore his nautical oilskins and gleamed when he moved like a plastic toad.

Time passed, we were steadily soaked, but no soldier-sailors arrived.

"The wheel's come off the hokey-pokey cart," said Private Drogue.

[130]

"Or the macaroni's got lashed up in the back axle," said Private Spool.

There was a hopeful portent at 21.45 when a train of two dozen mules, Andalusian, Mark IV, came over the ridge. They were loaded to the ears, piled so high with baggage that they lumbered through the darkness like shadow-elephants.

"Ah! *Buono!* said Captain Demoli. "Is our rations."

As we moved forward the top sack on one mule came to life, a man jumped to the ground, took one look at us and made off across the valley.

"*Alto! Alto-la!*" cried the captain. "I see you, Nicolo Pellochi. I order you come back here." He turned to me in explanation. "A bad man, a lazy man. Shoulda be marching with his comrades but he steala ride on the mule. Bah! That Nicolo Pellochi!"

We unloaded the mules. Thirteen carried sacks of onions, six were laden solid with raisins, four bore nothing but coffee beans and the remaining three were piled with feather palliasses.

"Something's gone wrong with your administration," I said. "Fifty-two hundredweight of onions. That's twenty-eight pounds per man."

"There has been a mistake. Always there are mistakes. But not to worry, *tenente.* For the *gloria d' Italia* we will eat the onions, we will live on the onions, we will fight and we will die eating only the onions . . ."

"You all breathe out together after golloping that lot," said Sergeant Transom, "and nobody'll never attack you."

Actually, the Solferino were lucky. All the Puccini Group with A Company got were twenty-eight mule loads of self-raising flour.

Came 22.00 hours and we went desperately to the head of the track. It was raining harder than ever but there was no sign of the relief column, no glutinous sound of marching feet. Each time I looked accusingly at Captain Demoli he shrank deeper into the shelter of his sou'wester.

"Our name's going to be flipping mud with them guards-men up there," said Private Drogue at 22.20 hours. "I can hear 'em sharpening their bayonets for us when we do get there."

"The worse thing, mate, one soldier can do to another," said Private Clapper, "is to be late for the take-over. Any mob done that to me I'd spit straight in their beer next time I see one of 'em."

At 22.45 hours Captain Demoli tapped my arm.

"Scusi, *tenente*," he said bright with a sudden curiosity, "but what will you do if my men don't come?"

I was that surprised, I nearly fell over. To a British military man like me it was an impossible question.

"Not come? . . . They've got to come. We're taking over from the Guards tonight."

"But *what* will you do if they don't come?"

"They've got to come. They just have to. Soldiers always come for a take-over. No matter what. . . . And why shouldn't they come?"

He spread his hands out to the beating rain, turned his face miserably up to the black sky, and shrugged doubtfully.

"Well, *tenente*. . . . It's a very wet night."

"What's that got to do with it?"

"Not a very nice night for walking, *tenente*. Not comfortable upon that track tonight. Not comfortable at all. Maybe my men take shelter in a farmhouse, under bridge, in a cave . . . keepa dry, sleep tonight and come on tomorrow. . . . Maybe, *tenente*," he added, cheered visibly by the prospect, "maybe it not rain tomorrow!"

I explained carefully to Captain Demoli the charges which could be levelled against a commander who brought his troops one day late for a take-over, described the pattern his court-martial would follow and ran through the composition and drill of the firing squad which would eventually shoot him at dawn. As his prospects of jeopardy grew, his anger mounted at his missing men.

"Madonna mia! That they should do such a thing to their *capitano.* Why they not here when I tella them come? Why they spit on the honour of Giuseppe Demoli? When they come with my bare hands will I taka my revenge . . ."

"Then you can start right away," said Sergeant Transom, "but you'll have to pick some of the poor perishers up before you knock 'em down."

It was then, at 23.00 hours, that the Solferino Liberation Group came toiling into the valley. They struggled up the track, as orderly as refugees, with mud caked all the way up their knee-length gaiters. They were loaded higher than the mules, carrying on their suffering backs machine guns, mortars, mandolines, ammunition boxes, tents, bugles, chianti, cooking pots, folding stools, flags of all colours, and every mortal thing needed to maintain an Italian formation in the field other than thirteen mule-loads of onions, six of raisins, four of coffee beans and three of feather palliasses.

Captain Demoli floundered through the mud to meet them, torrents of Neapolitan abuse bursting from his every seam, flecked here and there with English malediction to keep us in the picture.

"Are you cripples? Are you tortoise with legs broken? Two hours you keepa me standing in the rain. Two hours you keepa the *Garda Inglesi* waiting for take-over. Why you not each and every one of you cutta your throat? Why you not killa yourself before you comea late for the war and throw dirts on the *gloria d'Italia?* Better for you be dead on the ground than makea court-martial for Giuseppe Demoli!"

As his men stumbled past him each threw back a brief Italian denunciation of a sea captain who could bring his crew to such land-locked purgatory. They sank to rest upon the stores dump, pleading to their patron saints for the quietus of death. Which indulgence stoked the quarterdeck to gibbering point and, before any heavenly action could come to pass, he was among them with his riding boots, driving them back on their feet and into a ragged parade. Officers

[133]

and N.C.O.'s, dressed overall with rainbows of ribbon and insignia, flurried hither and thither on the gusts of their master's rage.

It was clear that he was well short of his expected two hundred and we'd have to make up *ad hoc* platoons. Someone brought him a box, three feet high, to stand on and he set to calling the roll.

We were now soaked to the socks, at that point of rain fatalism when water fills the inside of your boots and peace of mind comes from the knowledge that life can get no worse. It was a strange experience standing there in the dark, wet, and dangerous night, listening to the liquid Italian names rolling operatically up to the sky like a midnight pay parade at La Scala, Milan. The final names at last came up.

"Pascale Terroni . . . *Si* . . . Enrico Morrelli . . . Enrico Morrelli? . . . Bah! Yet another yellow-liver should have sucked poison at his mother's breast . . . Domenico Forasseti . . . *Si* . . . Nicolo Pellochi . . . Nicolo Pellochi? . . . Answer me, Nicolo Pellochi . . . I have seena you here, Nicolo Pellochi! . . . Answer me when your *capitano* calls!"

He dropped his nominal roll and raised his fists quivering above his head. This was the end! Forty-three men had not turned up. Half the arrivals had been dozy in making reply. And now Nicolo whom he had seen with his own eyes had gone absent, fallen asleep, or contracted dumb insolence.

"Nicolo Pellochi!" he called through clenched and furious teeth.

The night made no reply.

"*Nicolo Pellochi!*" Apoplexy was pumping him like a bull-frog and his officers moved back to give him room to burst.

"NICOLO PELLOCHI!"

He screamed at full blast of his lungs, towering his vengeful hands out into the rain, jumped once in airborne exasperation on his box . . . toppled this way . . . then that . . . and with a Pagliacci cry of tragic frustration fell flat on his face in a foot-deep morass of mud. A great moan of commiseration

[134]

went up from his command and everybody milled around in the swamp trying to pick him up.

"Good God Almighty!" said Sergeant Transom. "They'll wake the Jerries across the river if we don't get 'em out of here. He's got a line on this valley."

And he set to bellowing at the Italians in the grossest parade-ground English, making the traditional comments upon their birth, sloth, and physical deformity with such ferocity that, although they could not have understood a word he was saying, they froze automatically into three rigid and impeccable ranks. Which maneuver demanded that they drop their spread-eagled commander from a height of three feet back into his puddle, where he floundered and thrashed like a mud-bound octopus. In the interest of Allied goodwill I went personally to his assistance. Distrusting my intent after the treatment of his own troops he grappled me like a drowning man and we wrestled in the slough for some time before I got my hammerlock on and lugged him out.

We were now alone in the valley and a rugby referee would have been useful to get the mud out of our eyes. Captain Demoli was sobbing impotently to himself as we made our way up the hill towards the Guards command post. Sergeant Transom met us half way to report that the available Solferino had been broken into suitable parties and the take-over was almost complete. Sitting the captain on a convenient rock out of earshot I took the opportunity to point out to Sergeant Transom how wrong he had been to lose his temper and swear at our cobelligerents. Not only was such abuse of our new Allies in direct opposition to Government policy but, had my plans not been laid with such special attention to inter-Allied relations, it might well have ruined the whole take-over. I know that he took my advice to heart because I distinctly heard him, as he walked away, asking God to give him patience. And he was not, normally, a religious man.

By 02.30 hours all positions had been inspected and I settled to sleep in my headquarters cave. Suddenly, as though through some vast amplifier with echo box attached, the night was filled with a chorus of booming, one-foot-in-the-pub-door baritones singing "Largo al Factotum."

"Stand-to!" I cried. "Turn out the guard! It may be some devilish German trick."

"If it is," said Gripweed, my batman, "we should be all right. They've all had a skinful."

He was right. As we came out of the cave the glee club soared up with the bleary vibrato of Naafi-type Nellie Deans.

> . . . *Figaro qua, Figaro la!*
> *Figaro qua, Figaro la!*
> *Figaro so, Figaro giu!*
> *Figaro so, Figaro giu!*
> *Pronto prontissimo, son come il fulmine,*
> *Sono factotum della citta, della citta,*
>   *della citta, della citta!*
> *Ah, bravo Figaro! bravo bravissimo!*
> *Ah, bravo Figaro! bravo bravissimo!*
> *A te fortuna mon manchera. . . .*

The source of the song was away over on our left flank where the cliff softened and Corporal Dooley with two sections of Twelve Platoon commanded the only possible path to the river. The number of singers seemed to grow strangely less the nearer we got to the position.

"It's them Wops," gasped Gripweed as we scrambled on. "They're singing in Italian."

At which the curtain came down on the *Barber*.

"Anda now," rolled drunkenly up from below, "We singa for Tommy *Inglesi . . .*"

And the gorge of the Garigliano, already made fearful by Figaro, rang from wall to wall with the plastered tumult of a pidgin-English "God Save the King."

[136]

"There's only one of them, sir," said Corporal Dooley. "He's got down in the gorge somewhere and it's the echoes building him up like a choir."

"If he don't belt up soon," said Private Spool, "Jerry'll give us a stonk just to put us out of our misery."

A bottle smashed somewhere below, and for his fourth chorus the singer moved up to alto and Our Gracious King was interceded for in the drum-piercing tones of Jerry Colonna.

"Who on earth is it?" I asked.

"I tella you who it is, *tenente.*" Captain Demoli, mud-brown as a bear, came panting up with two midshipmen. "He's gotta hisa name written red-hot ona my heart. . . . He try to make madness for his *capitano.* . . . Allaways he getta drunk . . . allaways he singa Figaro . . . *Figaro qua, Figaro la.* . . . And allaways he say very sorry, *capitano,* never do again, *capitano.* . . . But thisa time he go too far, thisa time with my own bare hands when I catch him . . ."

He screwed the head off an invisible hen.

"Who is it, *mon Capitan?*"

He clenched his fists to his chest and stiffened his lips to help face the words.

"Isa Nicolo Pellochi. He steala the chianti. He hidea down there . . ."

And followed by his midshipmen he set off down the rocks as the voice wailed into a last heart-breaking "God Savea" and applauded himself rapturously.

"*Und nun,*" he boomed gutturally. "Musica for *Tedeschi* . . . Bella, bella Lili Marlene . . ."

As the sad sweet song came lilting up, the rain lifted, the moon broke through the clouds and far away to our right we could see the brooding whiteness of Monte Cassino. Everyone suddenly thought of home and Twelve Platoon were softly, ruefully joining in the chorus when, just as he came underneath the lamplight for the third time, their soloist was abruptly stricken to silence. It was then, I judged, that his *capitano* caught up with Nicolo Pellochi.

The Boche had beads on us from all angles and movement by day was strictly forbidden. The Solferino late-comers arrived the following evening and, together with equal portions of onions, raisins and coffee beans, were distributed around the positions.

By the third night, we had everything shipshape and I was quietly engaged in making notes for my Memoirs when Captain Demoli, with his bodyguard of midshipmen, effervesced into the cave.

"Scusi, *tenente*," he panted. "Isa life and death. The *Tedeschi!* He crossa the Garigliano! He massa for the attack!"

"Where? We've heard no gunfire."

With shaking hand he poured himself a drink, tossed it down and spat it straight out when he found he'd made free with my blood mixture.

"Not attack yet, *tenente*. They come across the river. They hide up in the trees. My bravea Commando section do the nighta patrol, makea sure all clear on our front. Creepa like redskin. . . . Ssh! . . . No makea no sound . . ." He shuffled forward like Juniper in his Quasimodo period. "Lie quiet as puss-cat, listen like hawk. . . . They heara *Tedeschi* talking . . . *Donner und blitzen . . . Komm' hier, geh' da . . . Jawohl, mein herr . . .*"

"How many Germans are there?"

"*Molto, molto Tedeschi.*"

"Where are they? Show me on the map."

He spread his hands apologetically.

"I dunno know where on map. My Commando officer stay watcha the enemy. Send back with message the heart of the lion who found the *Tedeschi*, the ears of tiger who hear them talk, the bravea hero of the Solferino who will lead us there— Nicolo Pellochi!"

"I thought he was your archenemy?"

He wriggled his head sentimentally.

"Ah! That Nicolo. In peace, the rascal. In war, the Garibaldi!"

Urgent investigation was obviously necessary. Sergeant Transom was touring the positions. I left a message for him, put on my leather jerkin and set off with my faithful batman. It was a long and tortuous way through the woods that the Commando had patrolled. We twisted and turned all ways in the darkness, scrambling among rocks, crawling through scrub, wading knee-deep in streams.

"The Solferino lot may be all right out on the Mare Nostrum," whispered Gripweed after an hour of blind crosscountry, "but tonight they've either been playing Hampton Court Maze or getting plain lost."

I had tried to follow our route on the map but its convolutions soon defeated me. From the way we kept doubling back, Maigret might have been on our tail.

"Psst!" hissed Captain Demoli as we burrowed a channel through a featherbed of compost. "We are near."

The Commando officer, who wore two pearl-handled pistols, a girdle of grenades, a dagger at his hip, and dirks in either sock, led us forward.

"He'd have a knife in his moosh," breathed Gripweed, "if he hadn't got false teeth."

We stopped under a long overhang of rock and listened. For a minute all was silent. Then, right above us, I heard stealthy movements, the rustle of leaves and guttural Teutonic whispering. . . . It was the Boche, all right. . . . Maybe just a patrol . . . maybe lying up for a dawn attack. . . . First thing was to fix their position . . . If I could get a bearing on Cassino or some other land mark. . . . Carefully I lifted myself up under the rock until I could see the horizon.

"*Hände hoch!*" rasped a voice behind us. . . . Bayonets pushed out from the bushes ahead. . . . Machine gun muzzles poked down from the rock above. . . . There was a scurrying

[139]

among the trees where Pellochi and the midshipmen had waited and then our hiding place was surrounded by a dozen soldiers with woollen hats, blackened faces, and wearing camouflage jerkins.

"Gawd!" said Gripweed. "We're in the bag."

Demoli and his lieutenant burst into fountains of placatory Italian.

"Steady, chaps," I said. "Remember, name, rank, and number only."

Resistance was clearly useless and I led them out from under the rock. I don't speak German but I had consigned to memory a few phrases suitable to such a situation.

"Ich bin ein Owzier. Bitte, nehem mir an dein Kommandant."

"Hände hoch," repeated the enemy in reply.

They closed around us, jabbing their guns in our backs and marched us up a goat track. I decided as we clambered towards captivity that I would study law while in prison camp. After making every possible effort to escape, of course. After ten minutes we came to a farmhouse built into the mountainside. They pushed us through a door and into a candle-lit room where a giant of a close-cropped Prussian sat at a map-strewn table. He was wearing a brown sweater and the flickering wax-light threw up the sabre-scar on his cheek.

I took off my jerkin to show the pips on my shoulders. The Boche respect strength of character so I decided to show my mettle from the start.

"My name," I snapped, "is Ernest Goodbody, my rank is substantive Lieutenant, my number is 131313."

"And I," said the Prussian in purest Oxford, "am Major Jan Kapolowski of the Warsaw Regiment, the Third Carpathian Division of the Second Polish Corps. Sorry my men mistook you but few of them speak English, and these two chaps with you are in very strange uniforms. And if you really want to bring your patrols back through our lines, it would be safer to let us know."

[140]

The Poles had not been in Africa and I'd never met one face to face before. I had no call to be doing so now since, according to the map, there were one company of the Musketeers and half a battalion of Black Watch between my right flank and the nearest clump of Carpathians.

I quickly explained that my inexperienced Italian foot-sailors had lost themselves on patrol and that, on locating them, I found that the only practicable way back was to lead them through the Polish lines. The major was utterly charming about the whole affair and ran us as far towards home as his jeep could make it.

As we plodded back up our approach track, Captain Demoli steadily cursed the name of Nicolo Pellochi.

". . . Why that dam-a-fool not listen? He singa Lili Marlene, don't he? He know when *Tedeschi* talking. . . . Is nota imbecile, is nota baby in arms. . . . Then why he come back say Polish soldiers speak like *Tedeschi?* . . . I tella you why . . . because he wanna make big fool out of his *capitano*, thatsa why. He wanna revenge, that Nicolo Pellochi, for when I choppa him down at sing-song. . . . Thisa time, that lousy sonofabitch, he go too far. Thisa time with my bare hands . . ."

He broke off as small-arms fire burst out on our front. We were still half a mile away but could see the bright swoop of tracer beating down from the machine guns of the central Italian position.

"To battle stations!" I commanded. "At the double. We're being attacked after all."

We made all speed the mud would allow and as we came in the back door of the stone barn, Sergeant Transom dropped through a side window. All the Italians, urged on by their officer with drawn cutlass were lining the forward wall and blazing away for dear life.

"Stop!" yelled Sergeant Transom. "Cease fire! *Niente tiro! Silenzio!*"

I wondered at first, as he lay about the defenders, pulling

them back from the loopholes and kicking their guns to the floor, whether he had gone over to Hitler.

"Steady, Sergeant," I said. "You'll have us overrun."

He wrenched our last firing defender from his post and now the only gun fire to be heard was coming from the attackers. It was a solitary machine gun firing half-hearted bursts.

"Listen to that," said Sergeant Transom. "A bloody Bren. One of ours, I'll lay a dollar. We're fighting among our flamingselves. . . . Come here, Captain Demoli, and yell out through this loophole who you are . . ."

As the captain shouted the Bren stopped firing and answering cries of liquid Italian relief came up from the enemy.

"*Madonna mia!* Isa my own Commando section coming back. The firsta bullets we fire, we shoot ourselves. Idiot! *Traditori!* Why you not usa your brains?"

He turned on his expostulating platoon commander and cuffed him out of the barn with the flat of his own cutlass.

"All-a-ways the mistakes. Never no *gloria d'Italia*. Why nobody tell him the Commando go out on patrol? Why don't he say halta-who-goes before shooting everybody? Why don't I killa myself like a Japanese? . . ."

The Commando section came straggling out of the darkness and paired off in voluble debate with the defenders.

"Scusi, *tenente*," said the two-gun commander. "Isa that Nicolo Pellochi. He say I leada you back shortcut same way as *capitano*. I trusta him. I takea his word . . . and he damned nearly getta me killed!"

He held out his beret to show where a bullet had snipped a foot off his scarlet plume. The fatal name turned the captain purple.

"Nicolo Pellochi!" he groaned, reaching out his hands for a throat to strangle. "Where isa that Judas-a-snake-in-the-grass? Where isa that Nicolo Pellochi?"

He looked fruitlessly around the barn and then ran out

into the darkness and down the hill in search of high noon with Nicolo.

"It's a good job," said Sergeant Transom as we walked back to our command post, "that those Ities can't shoot straight. There wasn't one of them got scratched even. If you leave out nancy-boy's ostrich feather."

I had barely started breakfast next morning when Major Arkdust came on the field-telephone.

"What the hell are you doing up there?" he demanded. "Trooping the Colour? The whole line from here to Cassino has been on the blower. If you don't call off your blasted church parade, they reckon you'll have the Boche getting jumpy and stonking all along the line. Didn't I make it plain enough to you? Absolutely no movement whatsoever by day."

"You did, sir. I'll investigate right away."

Sergeant Transom came down from the O.P.

"It's the Ities again, sir. Half of 'em, I reckon, parading down in the valley. We'll have to take a chance and get back there."

It was one of the more amazing sights of my war. Two hundred yards back from the front line, some hundred and fifty foot-sailors were drawn up in a hollow square. In its centre, on a catafalque made of a barn door raised on massed sacks of onions, lay a coffin draped by the red, white, and green of the Italian flag. Highly coloured officers formed a guard of honour at each corner of the bier, heads bowed in melancholy, hands folded reverently over cutlasses pointed in the ground. Four drummers rolled a requiem rataplan on muffled raisin barrels. A trio of bugles, muted as bagpipes, played a doleful threnody. The body of the troops stood with arms reversed, eyes downcast, and were keening a long, thin dirge.

"Gawd Strewth!" said Sergeant Transom. "A full-dress military funeral! And under the eyeballs of Cassino."

Captain Demoli came towards me from the head of the

[143]

parade. He was wearing a purple sash, a black band on either arm and carrying a missal.

"Isa good of you, *tenente,* to come paya your last respects. We bury our comrade. The firsta hero of the Solferino. The heart-of-a-lion who lay down his lifebloods for the *gloria d'Italia.* We make for him the military funeral."

"But you're in full view of the Germans. They'll shell us to bits."

He drew himself proudly up to his full rotundity.

"The Italian Navy must honour its dead. The *Tedeschi* see we make funeral parade. They respecta the dead. And we are at the end. You will salute the hero of the Solferino? . . . Please? . . ."

I looked at Sergeant Transom. He shrugged.

"They've gone to a lot of trouble," he said. "And if one does come over at least there'll be a grave handy."

We marched with Captain Demoli to the grave already dug beside the catafalque. As they lowered the flag-covered coffin into the pit, the bugles whispered a sad Italian Last Post and we whipped up salutes fit for the passing of a queen. The Boche never fired a shot. He probably couldn't believe his eyes.

"When was the poor chap killed?" I asked as the parade dispersed, leaving the sextons erecting the headstone.

"Last night, *tenente,*" replied Captain Demoli. "With the gallanta Commando."

"Who was he?"

The tears came to his eyes and his voice broke like puberty.

"Wasa my friend," he said sadly. "He was here in my heart allaways . . . wasa Nicolo Pellochi."

Chapter Twelve

Every time any of us went home to England we were struck by the intensity of the hatred of the enemy . . . the people were under a daily barrage of propaganda. Since they had no direct physical contact with the Germans, the German soldier was little by little invested with a monstrosity and savagery that was almost inhuman. . . . The experiences of the soldier in the field up to this point were, in the main, quite different. As soon as he met a German prisoner he observed that to all outward appearances he was a normal human being. A bit pompous, perhaps, and wooden, but still just another man. After the fight was over the reaction of the average soldier on seeing the prisoners was to think: "Well, the poor dumb beggars, they certainly bought it. They've had it." And he would hand out his cigarettes.

ALAN MOOREHEAD
Eclipse

DOWN IN CASSINO it was a private war. Your whole world was the Liri valley and the grey mountains bounding it were the ends of the earth. Reality was totally enclosed and no one was fighting anywhere else. The object of life was to conquer the Kafka symbol of Monte Cassino and put out the omniscient eyes of the Monastery.

In March 1944, Twelve Platoon crouched in the rubble of the station, while five hundred aircraft dropped a thousand tons of bombs in three and a half hours, many of them, fortunately, on the abbey and the enemy over the way. So battered was Cassino before they started that the best O.P. in the station looked out through the skirting ventilator of the exladies' lavatory. After the bombers were done, the earth was so gouged by craters and precipices that Hillary and Tensing would have wanted a leg-up to get through. With the tanks stuck uselessly outside, beaten by our own devastation, the rain returned in torrents and the March attack fizzled out. The infantry settled down again in April to the intimate, troglodyte combat which was the accepted Cassino way of life.

The Musketeers took their turn with everybody else to live cheek by jowl with the Germans in sewers, cellars, and fortified ruins; which places we shared with stagnant water and attendant rats, grateful to hide ourselves in the first and down with the second to escape from the oppression of the Monastery and the snipers in the Continental Hotel.

It was a curious type of warfare, skirmishing yard by yard along tunnels and culverts, mouseholing hopefully from house to house, and it was really better fitted to night-sighted ferrets than twentieth-century man. Nobody came out of their warren except by night, and by day an endless smoke screen drifted gloomily up the mountainside. There was always something rather improper about having the enemy as your next door neighbour. It was a real military embarrassment to be burrowing forward yourself on one side of the fireplace and to hear him start picking his way through on the other. Positive slum warfare ensued when the overcrowding got so bad that both sides had rooms in the same house. And we had to adapt ourselves to fighting in three dimensions when Twelve Platoon was residing in a comfortable basement flat off the approach road to Castle Hill, and the Germans found a way through the upper story remnants to occupy the floor above.

They made a lot of noise upstairs and Sergeant Transom banged on our ceiling with a rifle butt to let them know there were people trying to sleep down below.

"Bloody lodgers," he said. "All the same, you'd think

[146]

they'd keep it a bit quiet seeing they know we're all in night work."

We tried shooting through the ceiling and they tried shooting through the floor but there was about three feet of rockwork between us and all we got for our troubles was a basement buzzing alive with ricochets. They started pouring petrol down to soak through our stucco preparatory to baking us in our jackets, but Private Drogue got a match to it first, and from the ensuing hullabaloo overhead, they caught the blowback and for half an hour or so enjoyed under-floor heating fit for fire walkers. We finished up with a lampblack, soot-icicled ceiling. It not only looked right contemporary, but it also helped us to see better the whites of the rats' eyes.

Next, they tried to put the bailiffs in by digging down through to us. But every time they started in with the pickaxe, we began digging up from our end in exactly the same place. There's nothing so upsets a man digging down as to find someone from below cutting the ground from under his feet, and they soon gave up excavating.

We tried smoking them out through the rubble by building rag fires in chandeliers of M & V tins. Although we raised some heavy churchyard coughing overhead, we had to abandon the attack because the down draught turned our basement into a suffocation chamber.

"You'll have to give over fumigation, sir," choked Corporal Dooley, "or you'll finish up with a platoon of two-legged kippers."

The enemy struck back with the lodger's traditional trump. They brought up a gramophone and, working in relays, held a forty-eight hours, nonstop, Frau Braun Knees-Up and Bavarian National Clog Dancing Festival. The din was terrible down in our house, the tin-can chandeliers trembled to the beat and it was like living inside a marble kettledrum. We stood this vicious, mental warfare as long as our migraines could bear it, but on the second night, when the ceiling began to dribble clouds of brickdust, we felt it best to beat it back to a nearby coal cellar while a Sapper friend of Sergeant Transom's loaded the place with ammonal and blew the maisonette into a bungalow.

After living *à la* rabbit in the valley it was an eerie experience going up, in the second week of May, to take over the exposed pinnacle of Castle Hill. On a rocky sugarloaf, about four hundred yards to the north of the town, stood the remnant of a tenth-century castle, by crow a thousand yards from the Monastery, and our ultimate advance, so far, towards it. A craggy three hundred feet high, it piked impertinently up at the seventeen hundred feet bulk of Monte Cassino. The razor-edge path to the castle defeated mules and was commanded from both sides by the Germans. The summit area was perhaps as big as a tennis court, and the houses you looked down on were held by the enemy. There was nowhere to dig on the rock-bound platform and the sanitary problem of personal refuse disposal produced the most novel and satisfying method of attacking the enemy which I encountered throughout the war. Your solid sample was deposited in a sandbag which you dropped over the western precipice on to the roofs of the Boche dwelling below. At the best-sheltered spot for jettison, protected by the shell of the watchtower, some precisionist had built a bomb-aimer which enabled your gift to plaster on any selected roof without exposing your person in any unsafe or unseemly manner.

It was perhaps fitting that the strange and hazardous pinnacle of Castle Hill, the most forward salient of the Cassino line, should be the scene of one of the greatest single-handed coups of my military career. With the six-feet thick fragment of the watchtower curved before us, the sangars built among the ruins, and our tiny target space, we were reasonably safe from enemy artillery. It was our own guns that gave us the trouble. We could philosophize about the occasional H.E. clipping our crest from behind but the smoke shells drove us up the wall. Regularly, endlessly, they hissed over to keep the screen going in the valley, sometimes falling where intended, sometimes dropping the empty shell case our way, and sometimes presenting us with the reeking canister. They didn't score all that many direct hits on our plateau, but they kept us good and jumpy with near misses. The shell case could kill you outright and the canisters, in an unfavourable wind, could treat you to a more leisurely dose of asphyxiation.

I was engaged after lunch on May 16 for some few minutes on an urgent private matter and was preparing myself to proceed with my sandbag towards the bomb-aimer when I heard the familiar thresh of a short-falling smoke canister. As the sound came closer my experienced ear judged that it was almost directly overhead and aiming to land squarely on the spot where I sat. As rapidly as a lumbered Lothario I adjusted my dress and dashed for the nearest sangar. Hobbled as I was, I would have made it had not the canister changed direction in the wind and followed after me. . . . I turned for the shelter of the watchtower . . . the missile swooshed past my right ear, thumped to the ground a yard away and roared a tempest of smoke up into my face. . . . Blind-stifled and trouser-hampered, I leapt away . . . trod on my trailing braces, lurched on lastic-trapped feet, skidded on the rock around the bomb-aimer, and plunged over the side of Castle Hill and down into the valley below!

I landed upright, twenty feet later in a slope of soft scree . . . it began to flow under my weight, bearing me steeply downwards in a quickening avalanche. I gabbled a quick prayer that my landfall would not be on any of our "bomb"-plastered roofs and, fortunately, had the presence of mind to toss away my own sandbag. . . . Digging my hands into the running shale and squatting for fuller friction I scrabbled desperately to stay my descent . . . but there was nothing to grip, no branches to grasp, and like coke through a chute I sailed slowly over the next lip and down to the first flat ridge below.

As the roofs came up to meet me I thought it was Goodbody's Last Farewell. Then I hit the ground and found my fall broken by a vast, hairy beach ball . . . there was a blast on some mighty tuba . . . vapour of a fantastic vileness filled the air . . . I bounced off my air mattress and found myself rolling among four hooves. I had fallen on a day-dead mule, and the gas balloon of its inflated stomach had served as my trusty trampoline.

Spandaus opened up ahead and Brens spoke back from behind me. Bullets ripped along the track from both directions and I squirmed away from the graveyard of mules and into the debris of the nearest house. The stone door pillars propped up the fallen roof beams, and I rolled through the opening and across the floor to finish up face to face with a sleeping German soldier.

I was unarmed and still rather *déshabillé*—my belt and jacket I had taken off for my last operation on Castle Hill. Swift as a panther, I tucked in my shirt and slipped my braces into place. Remembering Churchill's injunction that you can always take one with you, I picked up a chair leg from the rubble. . . . As I moved, the German woke up and his hand flashed to his greatcoat pocket. . . . Before he could reach his weapon I hurled my chair leg at his head. . . . I missed, unfortunately, and the missile boomeranged back at my left ear. His hand came out of his pocket and, as I braced myself for the bullet, he thrust a piece of paper in my face.

"*Kamerad!*" he said. "I surrender. I have *passierschein.* Here is Safe Conduct."

He was threatening me with one of the Eighth Army surrender leaflets which were dropped on the enemy to encourage the fed-up or faint-hearted to turn themselves in. . . . "Safe Conduct" they read in many languages, "The German soldier who approaches the Allied positions without arms and with this Safe Conduct is to be well looked after, to receive food, and be removed from the danger zone as soon as possible."

"I am very grateful to see you," he said. "I am 8421/E/79 Hugo Plum. I approach your Allied position without arms and am eager to be well looked after, receive food and be removed from the danger zone as soon as possible. Thank you so much."

I took the paper from his hand.

"On behalf of General Sir Harold Alexander," I said, "Commander of the Fifteenth Army Group, I hereby accept your surrender."

"Good. I do it at last. For three days," he said aggrievedly, "I have been trying to get over to your lines, but all the time there is dangerous shooting outside. But now you have come to me. Now that you have captured this sector please remove me from danger."

The machine guns were still beating it up outside and as happened at Cassino when someone picked on somewhere, odd mortars, *nebelwerfers*, and gunnery were joining in from all over the place.

"I can't take you back till this lot dies down." I said, "You speak very good English for a German."

"I am not German. I am Austrian. I come from Salzburg and I never wished to make war on anybody. Do you know Leamington Spa?"

"Yes."

"Very nice, Leamington Spa. So peaceful." A little dark-haired man with the look of a hairdresser, he closed his eyes and sighed in sad memory. "Two seasons I play my cello in the Palm Court. I would much rather be in Leamington Spa than in Cassino, any day. Do you think there will be a prisoner-of-war camp at Leamington Spa?"

"I should think so."

"And do you permit orchestras in your prisoner-of-war camps?"

"Yes. The British Army is very keen on all forms of recreational training."

[151]

"Wundebar!" He looked at me hopefully. "Are you an officer? You have no jacket."

"I am an officer." My brain had been racing at top speed during this apparently aimless conversation, seeking a way of exploiting my situation. And, once again, logical analysis was rewarded by inspiration. "In fact, I am the Advanced *Passerschein* Officer. It is my duty to contact sensible enemy soldiers like you who wish to take advantage of our Safe Conduct offer. I had to take my jacket off and leave it behind to get through a very small hole." I wriggled my shoulders in imitation of a bottlenecked mole.

"The *Passerschein* Officer! That is very good."

"Now tell me, are there many more chaps like you in the vicinity? Other people who'd like to give up and live in peace at Leamington Spa?"

"There are some that I know, hiding up here and there. I have comrades very tired. It has been too long, too hard. Poland, France, Russia, Africa, and now here."

"I quite understand. I will make a bargain with you. We cannot possibly get out of here till after dark. And it would be beneath my dignity as *Passerschein* Officer to return with only one applicant. If you will go back into your lines, contact your comrades of similar feelings, and bring me another half-dozen or so to make up a respectable party, I will take you all out of danger tonight. And then I will see that you are placed in prisoner-of-war camp at Leamington Spa and permitted to form a camp orchestra. . . . What do you say?"

"Wundebar! To play again the cello at Leamington Spa! I will put the word round right away."

"Be careful," I said. "There's a hell of a war going on outside now."

"Have no fear. I never go near no danger. We have very safe way." And, humming "Liebestraum" with the bronchial boom of his instrument, he slipped down three steps and crawled away through a tunnel. I spent the rest of the day

[152]

reflecting that there is no situation so foregone in failure that positive thinking will not reshape it towards success, and in anticipating the congratulations of Colonel Plaster when, already given up as missing, I returned to my headquarters with half a dozen prisoners captured single-handed. I could almost feel the weight of that third pip already on my shoulder.

At five o'clock, Plum popped out of the tunnel to be followed by three more Germans.

"Hier ist der Passerschein Offizier." He ushered each forward in turn and they presented me with their Safe Conducts. Only the last one, a crop-headed cubical man with the expression of a disgruntled rattrap, had any English.

"I am Kaporal Streich," he said doomily. "I come only because my comrades go and they leave me behind. If they do not want me then I give up."

"Are there many troops pulling out?"

"I do not know. But my pig friends are gone. I starve. Please to give me food as in *passerschein.*"

"You'll have to wait till we get back to the British lines tonight. If you behave well you shall have *wiener schnitzel* and *sauerkraut* when we get there." I had no arms with which to enforce discipline so I had to make do with promises. Plum, eager to help, relayed the *wiener schnitzel* prospect to the others who beamed and rubbed their stomachs plaintively.

"I have put round the word that you wait here," said the cellist. "Soon there will be others. Soon I will be in the peacefulness of Leamington Spa, yes?"

"Another two turn up and you shall have *passerschein* for the Palm Court."

I had to wait till after dark for the next arrival, but then they began to issue from the tunnel thick and fast. By half past nine Plum had made his quota more than twice over and I had captured fifteen voluntary prisoners.

[153]

"I have found already, *Herr Passerschein Offizier*," he said delightedly, "a pianist and a violinist. If only a viola turns up I will have already my Leamington Spa Quartet."

Kaporal Streich with gloomy Teutonic efficiency made out a nominal roll. He brought before me a gaunt, lank—moustache who walked with boots full of broken glass.

"He is called Rikitz. His feet are infested by bunions. He ask that he be looked after like *passerschein* promise and that British doctor better his bunions."

"Rikitz may rely that if he keeps up the pace into our lines his bunions will be bettered immediately on arrival."

I was getting them in order to leave cover at eleven o'clock when a full-scale artillery barrage was laid across our neck of Cassino. When it lifted after ten minutes and rolled steadily forward behind us, I sensed that this was not the usual harassing fire but was the prelude to a set-piece attack.

"We'll have to hang on a while," I said to Plum. "There's going to be a regular battle down in front."

Small-arms fire broke out, the rip of Schmeissers, the burping of tommy guns, and the bowling crack of grenades, and away below an infantry assault came in. We settled down to rest while they fought it out. The mist was drifting up from the marshes and, jacketless, I shivered in my shirt.

"You are cold," said Plum. "I will get you jacket."

He went down the tunnel and came back with a Jerry greatcoat which I slipped gratefully over my shoulders. The battle blazed around and about for three hours and more, and the lemon dawn was tingeing the sky when the last sporadic firing died away.

All Cassino became strangely silent. I moved cautiously out through the doorway and looked back at Monastery Hill. A party of a dozen or so Germans was moving down the lower slopes under a white flag of truce. No one fired from either side. It was all over. Cassino was ours.

"Right," I said to Kaporal Streich, "make a white flag and we'll move off now."

Somebody found a white shirt which they tied by the sleeves to a banister rail. With Plum as standard-bearer, I led my captives out on to the track. We all crouched along furtively, feeling like lawbreakers out under the Monastery in the light of day. I decided to head for the Jail where the Musketeers' headquarters was located. The tottering finger of brickwork which marked it from the surrounding desolation had vanished during the night and I became sadly lost amid the gaping maze of craters in the centre of the town. It was a teeth and toenails job to get out of them and we lost all direction down in the bottoms. Some were sheer as a wall of death and passable only by birds, and others, as we approached the river, turned us back on our tracks with six-foot sumps of gobbling mud.

After almost an hour of circular mountaineering we picked up a clear track somewhere around the backyard of the Baron's Palace. My little band of peacemakers grumbled incessantly about the hardship of their journey to the promised land. I think their feet must have got soft sitting there on the defensive all that time at Cassino.

"Up and down," brooded Kaporal Streich as he came on hands and knees out of the last crater. "Round and round in rings. This is not being well looked after like in *passerschein*."

"Bunions," moaned Rikitz in simple misery. "So painful, painful, my bunions."

A platoon of South African soldiers came up the track towards us.

"Good morning," I said to the giant Boer sergeant at their head. "Could you please direct me to the Jail."

"The Jail, man?" he pondered. "Oh! I get you . . . just keep on down the track and you'll come to it."

As we limped on down the rocky path other small groups of surrendering Germans joined us. I heard Plum explaining importantly to each of them that they were now under the auspices of the *Passerschein* Officer and heading straight for *wiener schnitzel, sauerkraut,* chiropody, and instant Nirvana. My original dozen had grown to forty within twenty minutes and I led them on as fast as their feet would allow, spurred by the picture of Colonel Plaster's grateful amazement when I reported so vast a bag. The capture, single-handed and unarmed of forty prisoners might well constitute some sort of record in the Wisden of World War II.

We were passing the fragrant smell of a field kitchen frying bacon when I saw that it was in the shell of the Barracks away on the northern outskirts of the town, and I picked up my bearings. We were a long, long way past the Jail.

"You see," said Plum proprietorially, "the good *Passers-chein offizier* brings us to be fed."

"The roasting pork!" Streich sniffed ecstatically through his flattened nostrils. "The roasting pork! My stomach comes to life again."

Rikitz pointed to the Red Cross flag of a field dressing station.

"And the *doktors*. British *doktor* for bettering the bunions."

A military police corporal and four Nigerians with fixed bayonets came towards us.

"Good morning, Corporal," I said. "I am . . ."

"*Achtung! Achtung!* Me fine old load of superman," he bellowed. "Let's have yer, now! At the double through here."

The Nigerians came at my party like sheep dogs, jabbing the air emphatically with their bayonets. All forty surged suddenly forward and carried me with them through the gate which the corporal had opened in the barbed wire P. O. W. compound. Plum was last man in.

"For now we go in here," he said to the corporal as the gate slammed shut, "but tomorrow we go to Leamington Spa, yes?"

"Leamington Spa, mate? Never heard of it. You lot are going to Benghazi. You'll be over there making sand castles before the week's out.

The compound comprised a couple of thousand square yards of bare clay surrounded by eight feet of barbed wire. That was all. My personal prisoners looked around their barren home for any signs of Arcadia. Finding none, and waving their Safe Conducts like bilked bettors round a bookie they swarmed about me in protest.

"Is this to be well looked after like promises in *passerschein?*" snarled Kaporal Streich. "Where is the food that we are to receive? Where is the *wiener schnitzel?*"

"This is not hospital," cried Rikitz. "This is no place for infested man. Where are the doctors you promise for bettering bunions?"

"You tell me I go to Leamington Spa," shouted Plum, "but in your heart you plan to send me to Benghazi. I do not like Benghazi. Nobody never play the cello in Benghazi."

Plaints and vituperation were hurled up at me from every angle.

"Quiet!" I commanded. "I will talk to the corporal and straighten everything out," I fought my way through them to the fence. "Corporal," I cried. "I am a British officer. I am Lieutenant Goodbody of the Fourth Musketeers."

He came to the wire and a lance corporal followed him.

"British officer, eh? Then why are you wearing Jerry uniform?"

I looked down at myself and realized that I was still wearing the field-grey greatcoat that Plum had given me.

"Oh! I see your point. A pardonable error, Corporal." I unbuttoned the coat. "You see, I've got British shirt and battledress trousers underneath. I put on the greatcoat just to keep warm."

"Did you? You got any papers?"

"No. I left them in my jacket."

"Where's your jacket?"

"As a matter of fact, it's on top of Castle Hill. I had to take it off to . . . er . . . to attend to a personal matter. Then I fell off and captured this lot. . . . Single-handed, you know."

[157]

He sucked his teeth doubtfully.

"I don't know. You talk la-di-da English, I grant you and you got half a battle dress on. But I don't know . . ."

He put a hand on the gate.

"No!" shouted Streich. "Do not be cheated, corporal. This man is German soldier, just like us. He stole the trousers from a dead Tommy when he injured his own."

"Don't be stupid, Kaporal Streich," I said. "Tell them who I am."

"Aye-aye," said the lance jack. "He knows that Jerry corporal's name, don't he?"

"You got us here by tricks," hissed Streich to me. "You not keep your promises. So you stay suffer with us."

Plum joined in the Judas business.

"This man is not British officer," he said. "He wears half a British uniform only to spy upon your positions. He is dangerous German spy."

"He is the worst one," croaked Rikitz. "He is Waffen S. S. man. He kill wounded British soldiers. Many times now he plan escape in British uniform."

"But this is ridiculous," I cried. "I am Lieutenant Ernest Goodbody of the Fourth Musketeers. Do I look like an S. S. man?"

"They're the rottenest bastards of the lot, the S. S.," said the corporal.

"And look at them nasty, beady eyes," said the lance jack. "Do in his own mother if Hilter gave the say-so."

"He's fatter than all the others, too. Proves he was in something special where they got the grub."

"I am a British officer, I tell you. Take me to . . ."

"He is not British officer," bawled Streich. "He is Waffen S. S. military spy. You leave him in here and we will deal with him ourselves."

My captured pack came baying around me and the corporal pushed open the gate and called in the Nigerian guards to keep the peace.

"Shut up!" he yelled. "Everybody sit down! *Sitzen-Sie!*
Sitzen-Sei! If you don't want a bayonet up your jacksie. And
you . . ." he pointed at me, "don't be trying any more of your
funny tricks. Or he'll have the ears off you."

And he posted a special sentry over me and left four others
to roam the compound.

The glory of my day was gone. My triumph was trodden
down to ignominy. Cassino had fallen, the battle was won,
my comrades in arms were roaring up the road to Rome, and
I, amid all the flames of victory, was sitting on the spikiest
square foot of a P. O. W. compound, imprisoned by the British, threatened by vengeful Germans, and personally guarded
by a black man obsessively anxious to blood-stain his bayonet.
The Boche seated on their hunkers all around me kept up a
low torrent of Teutonic curses at the man who dishonoured
their *passerscheins* to paradise and threw surreptitious rocks
at me whenever the backs of the guards were turned. Every
time I moved a muscle to retaliate or opened my mouth to
state my case to any sympathetic-looking passerby, my faithful Nubian made to fill it with a half a yard of bayonet. I
tried whistling "God Save the King" as a general distress
signal, but he took steely exception to this as well. My hand
semaphore, navy fashion, of S O S also earned his disapproval
and I had no option but to sit and suffer in the silent posture
of a martyred Buddha.

I was worried, not only about my own situation, but also
about the plight of Twelve Platoon, pushing on towards the
Eternal City without my guiding hand. Sergeant Transom
was no doubt developing steadily under my tutelage, but I
had not had opportunity to take him through my O. C. T. U.
notes on "The Breakthrough and Pursuit." Also I had prepared two lectures which I had intended to give when entry
into the capital became a possibility. One was entitled "A
Ramble in Ancient Rome" and the other was the standard
talk which I always gave when the Musketeers approached
any large city. "The Penalties of Promiscuity." Sergeant

[159]

Transom might possibly be able to deliver the first from the draft in my notebook, but I doubted very much whether his known weakness for foreign women would allow him to be convincing about the second.

For three hours I squatted immobile and pensive under the mounting sun and I was beginning to wonder what life would be like as an Anglo-German pariah in Benghazi when I heard the voices of Aryan pedlars working round the outside of the wire.

"Cigarettes . . . Chocolate . . . Any watches or cameras. *Zigaretten and Schockoladen für Kameras oder Taschenuhrs.* Cigarettes . . . Chocolate . . ."

Apart from their super-cinema identification there was something familiar about the hawking voices, but they were away behind me and I hesitated to look round lest my black guard took impaling offence. From the corner of my eyes I could see that one of the more liberal-minded sentries was allowing prisoners up to the wire to do business. Watches and the occasional camera sailed over the wire and the hucksters sent packets of cigarettes or bars of chocolate back in return.

"Cigarettes . . . Chocolates . . . *Zigaretten . . . Schockoladen . . .*"

The three pedlars with their kitbags of stock came abreast of my bed of nails and I saw with delight that they were Corporal Dooley, Corporal Globe, and Private Clapper. Without moving a muscle of my face lest I collect a mouthful of stiletto, I threw my voice their way, cunning and stiff-lipped as a ventriloquist . . .

"Corporal Dooley . . . Corporal Dooley. Lieutenant Goodbody here . . . Your platoon commander speaking. Rally on me!"

Dooley stopped in mid-barter of twenty Woodbines for a Leica, open-mouthed and petrified as a man hearing from a cloud the voice of his god.

"Corporal Dooley," I yoo-hooed in my sing-sing sidelong. "Twelve Platoon rally on me!"

He dropped the camera and came up to my neck of the fence.

"God love us all!" he said. "It's him! Sitting there with the Jerries like a brass-bound yogi."

"P'raps he's changed sides," said Corporal Globe." Gone over to persecute Hitler."

"I have been wrongfully arrested," I crooned. "They believe me a German. Find the officer in charge and tell him who I am."

The two corporals conferred.

"Just our luck," said Dooley. "Come back here with a load of prisoners and we have to find the governor."

"And the boys are going to be dead pleased when we turn up with him again, ain't they?"

"Overjoyed, Globey boy, bleeding overjoyed."

"Well then," I urged. "Get me out of here. The sooner you identify me the sooner can the men have me back in command."

"He's seen us," said Dooley. "There's nothing else we can do."

"You're right," said Globe. "And Benghazi is a bit much, ain't it. . . . Hold the sack, Clapper."

They went off to the commandant's office and Clapper leaned through the fence and placated my Nigerian with a handful of cigarettes.

"I hope you'll excuse me, sir, now that the others have gone, if I just take the opportunity to have a private word with you. I got the domestic trouble again."

I was sorely tempted to tell him that it was neither time nor place for welfare matters, but I realized the duty of an officer to be ready to help his men at all times and I curbed my tongue.

"I'm sorry to hear that," I said, shifting my buttocks through another five degrees so that the flints made acupuncture on new flesh.

"It's not, I trust, Mrs. Clapper again?"

[161]

"I'm afraid so, sir. She's getting laid again."

"But I thought we'd circumvented the passionate butcher by converting herself and your mother to vegetarianism."

"We did that butcher down, all right, don't you worry, sir. He never got no more under at our house after they joined the lettuce-and-nuts brigade. It's the Yanks this time, sir. A meat-hating mobile laundry top sergeant from Tacoma, Washington, met her at the vegetarian club. Comes round regular on his every half day, my mum says, with bunches of kohlrabi, endive, and other unusual vegetables, fills that poor little kid's head with tales of his oil wells and orange plantations and lays her something rotten on her own bridal bed. . . . Now is that right, sir, that's all I want to know, when a man's away in a foreign country fighting for liberty, equality, and democracy, that American laundrymen should come over to England and keep having their hoggins off his wife?"

"Decidedly not, Clapper. Not only is such lubricity bad for your marriage, but it is also ultimately damaging to Anglo-American relations. Now tell me, on what day of the week does this man have his half day to visit your wife?"

"Every Saturday afternoon. He's out mobile-laundering all the rest of the week."

"Then we must persuade your wife to find some employment in which attendance at work on Saturday afternoons is obligatory. Now let me see . . . what about working on the turnstile at football matches?"

"What about the summer? The war could go on a long time."

"Or a bus conductress?"

"They get every third Saturday off."

"She could work on a post office counter."

"Never no head for figures, sir. Not my little girl."

The Nigerian threw away his cigarette and spoke for the first time in our acquaintance.

" 'Ow abaht," he said in purest Cockney, "the old swim-ming barf attendant?"

Before Clapper and I had time to pass judgment on this suggestion, Dooley and Globe came out of the office with the key to the compound, closely followed by a provost marshal who was beating my expostulating military police corporal about the shoulders with the flat of his cap.

Chapter Thirteen

It was during this visit that Stalin, seeing one of his marshals being carried out, dead drunk, from a banquet, asked Eden whether British generals got drunk too, and added, "I find that, the more my generals drink, the better they are."

MAJ. GEN. SIR JOHN KENNEDY
The Business of War

The dinner-party was great fun. Monty drank water, but produced a bottle of good claret for me. He said, "I had a spoonful of white wine the other night, but I did not like it."

Ibid

A serious appeal was made to me by General Alexander for more beer for the troops in Italy. . . . Make sure that the beer—four pints a week— goes to the troops under the fire of the enemy before any of the parties of the rear get a drop.

PRIME MINISTER'S MEMORANDUM TO
SECRETARY OF STATE FOR WAR

TOTAL WAR IN ITALY was a slow grind up the narrow trunk and the breakout from Anzio was about the only time that anybody had a chance to attack across the grain. The thrust of the beachhead force aimed across country to cut the road back from Cassino to Rome at Valmontone. From fifty miles south the German Tenth Army was in flight before the Fifth and Eighth Armies coming up the warp after breaking Cassino and the Adolf Hitler Line. Just as the beachhead force, coming across the weft, was in striking distance of Valmon-

[164]

tone and the trap was about to close, they were suddenly ordered to change the direction of their main thrust, turn with the grain and head, in advance of the southern armies, straight for Rome.

The minds of historians and the consciences of generals have since been greatly exercised by controversy about the cause, wisdom, lunacy, credit, or debit of this strange decision which exchanged the destruction of the Tenth Army for the glamorous liberation of Rome. But it raised no polemics at the time among the troops actually involved. They were unconcerned whether the theoretical objective of their chinagraph puppet masters was Rome, Valmontone, or Timbuctoo. They were ever prepared, in the broad interests of peace, to advance in the general direction of the enemy, but their precise objectives were defined by that private inter-Allied battle which waged the length of Italy . . . the Battle of the Booze.

If it so happened that the routes of advance dreamed up by the Higher Command coincided with those required for Alcoholic Warfare, then so much the better for everyone concerned; if they did not, then too bad for the generals.

The main supply route from the rear was the Benevento Pipeline. No matter how far north the front line went, this vital liquor link was maintained by a continued chain of fifteen-hundredweight trucks running on illegal journeys southwards, a hundred miles and more, back almost to where the invasion began. This British pilgrimage flowed unceasingly because in Benevento they made gin. They may not have been the best ginmakers in Europe but, by God, they were the fastest.

Much against my principles, I was often sent back by Colonel Plaster down the Benevento Pipeline. I find I share many of my military views with Lord Montgomery and I am again one with him on the question of drink. If he is to think logically and act decisively, an officer must keep a clear head

[165]

at all times. I therefore confined my wartime drinking to that minimum made obligatory by state occasions.

"Sorry to keep sending you off to Benevento, Goodbody," the colonel would say, "but you're the only chap in the mess I can trust not to drink half the cargo on the way back."

When I took down the order for Captain Tablet's birthday I was instructed to call on a recommended distiller named Caesario who had his warehouse on the riverside.

"I want," I read from my list, "twenty litres of gin, twelve litres of whisky, and eight bottles of brandy."

"O. K. chief. You wanta all this stuff today."

"Yes. I've got to start straight back."

"Very sorry, chief. I giva you the gin, the whisky, pronto, right away. But I can't give you no brandy till tomorrow."

"Why not?"

He wiggled his humpback apologetically.

"Gin, whisky . . . I maka right away. But it taka me twenty-four hours to maka brandy."

I asked to see his instant distillery and he took me into his shed. As far as I could see, his total equipment was a hundred-gallon drum of industrial alcohol, a bottle of oil of juniper, a jar of burnt sugar, a packet of ground ginger and a witches-cruet of sundry herbs. He held up the juniper bottle.

"Maka gin, pronto." Then he displayed the sugar and ginger. "Maka whisky, pronto. . . . Buta the brandy, not so easy. The brandy I hava to boil all night."

Feeling faint for the linings of my comrades' stomachs, I cancelled the brandy and took on whisky in its place. Grateful for my gift of abstinence I watched in fascination as Captain Tablet's good-wishers downed every last drop of Caesario's lightning liquers. And wondrously enough, it didn't seem to affect them unduly at all. If anything, they broke slightly less furniture than usual.

The Benevento Pipeline only supplied the basic, spirituous rations of the forward troops. For their finer drinking they lived off the country, for their share of Italian ambrosia

[166]

they fought the Battle of the Booze. There were two sets of operational maps; one marked obediently with the boundaries, axes, and objectives of the generals; the other noted with the location of every vineyard, château, bodega, palazzo, castello, hotel, tavern, or sawdust bar within striking distance. In this secret battle every man's hand was against every man. Americans, British, Poles, Canadians, New Zealanders, and Frenchmen, all schemed and maneuvered one against the other to capture the citadels of Bacchus. No holds were barred, no boundaries recognized and the only limit on the length of poaching was the brazenry of a commander's neck.

Colonel Plaster was a keen connoisseur of anything alcoholic and he carried a copy of *The Wine-Lover's Guide to Italy* to ensure that nothing drinkable slipped his notice. He was bred to believe that niggers began at Calais and the only time he ever spoke to an Italian was to ask him if there were any good caches of vino in the vicinity. I plumbed the depths of his dedication to the Battle soon after the fall of the Hitler Line when the Musketeers were pushing on north of Arce. C Company was leading with Twelve Platoon out on the right flank charged with reconnoitering the village of Dolmino, and occupying it if it were abandoned by the retreating enemy. I kept the chaps going at good speed and when we arrived in the late afternoon we found Dolmino completely deserted.

"Lovely grub," said Sergeant Transom. "Made our bound by tea time. Jerry'll be away up the road and blowing the bridge at Pasto. We can get a decent meal going and have a night's kip under cover for a change."

I did not attempt to conceal my disappointment at his attitude.

"We must advance at once and reestablish contact with the enemy. Remember the colonel's closing words at every order group. . . . 'When in doubt, the Boche seek out!' "

"But if we push on too fast we'll leave the right flank exposed."

[167]

I smiled acidly and pointed to the dust clouds rising a mile or so to our right.

"The New Zealanders are already ahead of us."

We pushed on another two miles to the river Caroni and dug in for the night on the mud bank commanding the stumps of the blown bridge. It may not have been comfortable but our tactical siting was superb. I was happy to receive a message next morning requiring me to meet the colonel at company headquarters.

I saluted smartly, confident of his congratulations.

"Goodbody reporting, sir. Twelve Platoon is established on the line of the Caroni and commands a bridging site for the sappers."

"Why the hell aren't you back at Dolmino?"

"We took it early yesterday, sir, and pushed on. . . . You know, sir . . . 'When in doubt, the Boche seek out.' "

"Don't speak bloody poetry at me. I told you to occupy Dolmino, not win the blasted war. D'you know what's happened back there while you've been swanning up the road?"

"No, sir."

"The Musketeers have lost Dolmino."

"Good Lord, sir! I am sorry. When did the Boche counterattack?"

"Not the Boche, you bonehead. It's those damned Kiwis. They've come across the boundary and occupied Dolmino. They've got my vermouth factory! I'll never live it down!"

"Your vermouth factory, sir?"

"Yes. Why the hell d'you think I sent you to occupy the place?" He slapped the *Wine-Lover's Guide* on the table in emphasis. "Because it contains the biggest and best damned vermouth factory this side of Rome. You've handed it lock, stock, and barrel to the Kiwis."

"I'm very sorry, sir . . ."

"I don't want your sorrow. I want my vermouth. So you take your chaps back to Dolmino with a water cart and fill it up before the Kiwis make off with the lot."

The vermouth factory had a vast, stone storage vat as big as a church. There was already a queue of water tankers when I got there and I had to pay the New Zealand sergeant major in charge two thousand lire for a two hundred and fifty gallon fill. It took our topers about three weeks to finish the lot; and my teetotal principles were further fortified by the report that when the vat was finally drained, they found a dead German smiling seraphically at the bottom.

My third pip had clearly receded at Dolmino and it wasn't till the vermouth was running low that I got a chance to redeem my reputation. We were by then within forty miles of Rome and operating in the foothills of the Leprini Mountains, hoping to link up some time with the advance out of Anzio. C Company was in reserve when our commander called on us.

"I've got a job for you, Goodbody," he said, "and if I had another teetotaller in the Regiment, I'd not be using you. . . . I want you to take a flying column to Castello Montepico. It's about fifteen miles away . . . there on the map. . . . As you can see, the Yanks are approaching it from the west, the New Zealanders are coming up from the south, and we've almost got it outflanked to the east. The Boche will obviously be pulling out in the next twenty-four hours or so. Now I don't want you to attack the place. . . . Just get up as near as you safely can and race in the minute the Boche is gone. It is imperative that the Musketeers are first into Montepico. . . . Is that clear?"

"Yes, sir. And what vehicles will I have in my column?"

"Two half-tracks. They should take a couple of sections . . . and . . . ahem . . . a water cart."

I studied the map.

"But isn't the place in the New Zealanders' area, sir? It's a good ten miles wide of our boundary."

The fronds of his moustache rustled and his eyes glistened redly.

"Castello Montepico, my boy, knows no boundaries. It belongs to all the wine-lovers of the world. Since time immemorial, ever since the grape has grown, the finest Frascati in all Italy has been made there. Every vintage is a monarch but the emperor of them all is Montepico '92. It is still in cask at the castello and you'll recognize it by the date and three interlaced crowns branded into the wood . . . like this . . ."

And thus it became my mission to seek the top trophy of the Battle of the Booze, to seize the last of the Montepico '92 for the honour and intemperance of the Fourth Musketeers.

I hinted at the platoon order group that success in our assignment would enhance my prospects of promotion and my N.C.O.'s responded most loyally.

"If you got a third pip up, sir," said Sergeant Transom, "they'd have to make you second-in-command of a company and we'd lose you from Twelve Platoon, wouldn't we?"

"I'm afraid so, Sergeant. But, *c'est la guerre.*"

"In that case, sir, you can rely on everybody in the platoon doing their level best to get that booze."

"And I second that on behalf of the corporals," said Dooley. "Three bags full."

"Thank you," I said simply. "No matter where the ladder of promotion may lead me, I will never forget you chaps in good old Twelve Platoon."

When we set off at dawn next day the back of my command half-tracks was stacked out with notice boards and paint pots.

"What are all the signs for, Sergeant?"

"We're breaking new ground, ain't we, sir? Never know what signs you may need to help them that come after. The boys been up half the night doing that lot."

It was a good point; a primary duty of the advance guard is to mark up safe routes for following formations.

We ground along the twisting lanes into no-man's-land, driving slowly to keep down the tell-tale plume of dust. It was fine to be carried after the weeks of foot-slogging, but I felt in my stomach the infantryman's unease at being too far

[170]

from a ditch and was grateful for the head-high armour of the half-track. After an hour of cautious bounding from ridge to ridge we came up at a crossroads with a patrol of three armoured cars. A Kiwi lieutenant climbed down from his turret.

"You had the fear o' Gawd up me for a minute, mate," he said. "I thought them tracks of yourn was Jerry tanks. . . . Comber's the name . . . Musketeers, eh? What you doing out here in our territory?"

"I'm Goodbody," I said. "Just pushing on. Getting stuck into the old Boche, you know."

He had a broken nose and was husky enough for a full-back.

"You ain't belting for Rome, are you? First in for the Musketeers, like? Because you mustn't do that. You know we all got to hold off and let the Yanks be first into Rome. If they ain't allowed to liberate Rome, they're going to take their bat and ball home."

"We're not making for Rome. . . . We're on a sort of special mission."

"Special mission? Where to?" He noticed the water cart and suspicion hawked up his face. "Hey! You ain't making for Montepico?"

"Montepico? . . . Never heard of it . . ." I floundered, unprepared for such direct, inter-Allied interrogation. "As a matter of fact we're going across to see the Americans."

"What for?"

"Water," said Sergeant Transom. "They've got their only supply road blocked by a delayed-action bomb and we're taking a load of water to their forward company. Be seeing you in Rotorua."

The driver let in the clutch and made to drive on through the cross roads.

"Hold hard!" shouted Comber. "That's for Rome. You want to turn left for the Yanks."

There was nothing else for it but to turn left and drive on.

[171]

"Did you notice his column?" asked Sergeant Transom.

"Yes. Three armoured cars."

"And one with a water trailer behind it. This ain't going to be no cakewalk."

The road ran persistently southwest, bearing us at right angles to Montepico, and never a turning showed up to the right. We ran clear through the New Zealanders area and found in the first village we struck three Sherman tanks labelled respectively Lulubelle, Geronimo III, and Dodger's Delight. A gangling man in a Martian helmet came out of Lulubelle.

"Lootenant Maloney," he said, "and I don't spell it with a 'B.' Where you boys come from? I thought we had Australians or somebody on our right."

"Lieutenant Goodbody, Fourth Musketeers. Pleased to meet you."

"Are you now?" He waved to Lulubelle. "Limeys, fellers. Get the gun on 'em."

The turret came round and all barrels bore down on us.

"Now," said Maloney, "we can talk. . . . You guys wouldn't be after busting your way to Rome, would ya? General Mark Clark's gonna be first into Rome and we gonna see nobody else don't jump into the act. O.K.?"

"O.K. We don't want Rome. We just want some water. There's none in our forward area and the Kiwis can't help us."

"The river's just back there. You been driving alongside it for the last three miles."

"Really? Well, thank you very much. We'll get back there and fill up."

"You do that thing, brother, and then hightail it back to your own territory. My boys gonna reckon it mighty suspicious if they see you ratting around here again. And when they get suspicious, they get rough."

[172]

We returned the way we had come, followed by the traversing guns of Lulubelle.

"Get rough!" grated Private Drogue back among the signboards. "We'd have their bleeding guts for hamburgers."

"This job don't get no easier," said Sergeant Transom. "Maloney's old man sent him on the same kick as us. He's got a three-tonner up the road full of wine barrels."

When safely out of sight we stopped to consider our situation. We were trapped on our traverse road, the Yanks at one end, the Kiwis at the other. Their two north-running roads formed a triangle which met a mile below Montepico to join the only road up to the Castello from our side. There were odd lanes running across the triangle between these two roads, but nothing else northwards.

"We got to use one of those roads if we're going to make Montepico," said Sergeant Transom. "We'll have to make like the Goums and cut across country."

There was a long-rolling explosion far away to the north.

"That'll be a bridge going up. Jerry's on his way out. Those Kiwis with their armoured cars are the fastest. We'd better see if we can cut in front of them."

The rocky going wasn't bad for the half-tracks but we had to hitch a towrope on the water cart to keep it rolling. Luck turned our way after twenty minutes' pioneering and we hit a dry riverbed which carried us clear through to the Kiwis' road. The surface was white with wind-scattered dust and there wasn't a tire mark anywhere.

"We're ahead of them," I cried hearteningly. "Bash on, chaps, for Montepico!"

"Take it steady," said Sergeant Transom to the drivers, "they might have mines down. Stop if you see any signs that there's been digging on the road or any piles of leaves or brushwood put down to cover up digging."

I gave out a few hints of my own on anti-mine precautions and we rolled northwards. We met no mines, but after three cautious miles were halted by a crater, thirty feet across and six deep.

"It looks solid in the bottom," I said. "If we slope down the sides we could make it."

"But it'll take us best part of an hour," said the sergeant. "We'll have to hold off those Kiwis while we do it. . . . Corporal Dooley, get the detector out and sweep all round before anybody else gets down. Tape your safe area and check for booby lines. If all's well get digging on the edges. I'll be back in a quarter of an hour."

He turned our half-track and drove back down the road about half a mile to a point where it swept in a long curve between steep banks.

"Everybody off," said Sergeant Transom. Corporal Hink and our five men leaped down. "Now you know what to do. Corporal Hink and you three get mine-laying. Quick bash with the pickaxe every ten yards, lob in a couple of bottle tops, cover up with heaps of brushwood. . . . You two get them signs and follow me."

When we drove off back to the crater both banks of the road were festooned with warning notices . . . DANGER MINES . . . BEWARE BOOBY TRAPS . . . and two hundred yards of its surface was pocked with brushwood.

"That'll hold 'em," said Corporal Hink. "Nothing puts the wind up them armoured-car kings like mines. Every one of them bottle tops'll give a ping on the old detector and they'll never know if the next one ain't the real McCoy. They'll have half that road up before they push on."

"Pity we hadn't just one real mine to put down, just for luck," said Private Spool. "Bleeding Kiwi nicked a tart off me in Tunis. I wouldn't mind blowing him up."

After all hands had chipped away at the crater for another half hour we had a negotiable gradient on each side. Corporal Dooley ran down from his observation post at the top of the bluff.

[174]

"They're up to the last three bottle tops. That Kiwi lieutenant's doing a clog dance on the mine signs."

We piled in and roared off once again. Two miles farther on we came to another crater.

"It's bigger than the last," I said. "They'll be on us before we could get one side done."

"We'll have to get off this road," said Sergeant Transom. "There was a turning a bit back that would take us across to the other one."

He stopped the truck at the turning and got down. He drove a notice board into each bank of the main road and slung a length of tape in between. Each sign was a bright yellow disc with a black skull and crossbones.

"What do those mean?" I asked as we rolled down the side road.

"I don't know. But if you saw them, you'd stop and have a look around, wouldn't you?"

As we approached our junction with the American's road, we heard the clatter of tank tracks and the peak roaring of engines just to our south. We stopped our column and patrolled to the crest ahead. Down on the main road below we saw Maloney's convoy held up by a blown bridge. It was only a shallow stream and he was using his tanks to bulldoze rocks and tree trunks into the gap.

"That's a bit of luck, anyway," said Sergeant Transom. "But it won't hold them for long. They're damned good at road-mending, those Yanks."

We pushed along the road northwards and were within three miles of the junction below Montepico when we came round a bend and the road vanished into the mountainside. A clear slope of rock and rubble ran from the cliff on our left straight down into the valley below. The Boche had blown the overhang and the avalanche blotted out a hundred yards of road.

"Strewth!" said Corporal Hink. "We'd not get through

[175]

there by Christmas. I'd sooner dig the Mersey Tunnel. That lot's a job for the sappers."

There was no friendly turning this time and we made off across country again. We pulled off at a lay-by which had once been a dump for road-making materials and ground up a track among scrub and wild olives. Just out of sight of the road Sergeant Transom pulled up and disappeared into the trees.

"Got it!" he shouted after a couple of minutes scurrying around. "Just up here."

I joined him where he stood before a weed-lined ditch, about twenty feet square, with straight-cut walls some eight feet deep. The bottom was filled with brambles straggling in oozing, white mud.

"Well done," I said. "What is it?"

"You always find one of these near the road-mender's pull-in. It's a lime pit. They make lime cement as they go in Italy. Dig it out and cook it on site." He tossed a rock and the mud sucked it in gratefully. "Just the job for us, too. . . . Corporal Dooley, four men, get chopping branches to cover this hole . . . Corporal Hinks, get the tarpaulins out of the trucks . . ."

He spiked two signs on the road . . . DIVERSION—ROAD BLOWN . . . and mounted arrows pointing up the track, continuing in through the scrub to the lime pit. The pit was covered with a lattice of branches, tarpaulins laid on top and dressed with soil, rocks, and greenstuff so that we couldn't tell ourselves where the track ended and the hole began.

"That's the way they catch elephants in India," said Corporal Dooley. "Old Lulubelle gets down there and the heroes of Rome are going to have a sweaty half hour digging her out."

We drove on up the ridge, brushing out our track marks behind. Just over the hump we stopped and crawled back to look down on the trap. . . . Roaring at speed, Lulubelle came clattering round the bend, braked harshly as the driver re-

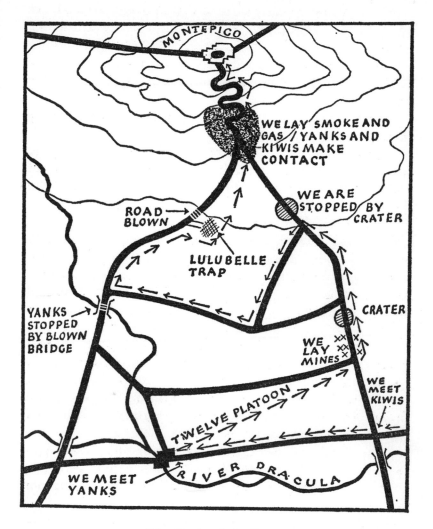

The Battle of the Booze

acted automatically to the diversion sign and swung across the clearing and up the track.

Lieutenant Maloney, magnificent as an All-American footballer in his antennaed helmet, protruded commandingly from the turret, shouting directions to his crew. He was turning, chin held at the approved MacArthur jut, beckoning his command to follow, when Lulubelle hit the lime pit, leaped a little in wild surprise, and disappeared from view. Geronimo III skidded to a crashing stop on the brink and Dodger's Delight, lacking the quick, animal reaction of the Redskin, clanged mightily up his tail feathers. . . . Maloney must have missed his footing getting out because he scrambled up out of the pit whitewashed to the waist.

"Limeys!" he yelled. "It's those goddammed Limeys after that vino!"

We mounted and beat it down into the next valley before Maloney's language burnt all the oxygen out of the air. The plain running down to the vital road junction was sewn with dragon's teeth and it was slow going for the water cart. By the time we got over the last bone-breaker and rose up the road to Montepico, we could see the Shermans half a mile away hammering up Maloney's branch of the fork, and the dust cloud of the New Zealanders away in the distance down the other.

"Jerry's gone all right," said Sergeant Transom. "Otherwise he'd be stonking them Kiwis. . . . We'll have to make ourselves a bit more time . . ."

He stopped and got down with Corporal Hink and a box of grey cylinders.

"Smoke canisters," he said. "Left over from when we had to lay 'em at Cassino. Knew they'd come in handy."

They went down to windward of the junction, made a petrol splash fire and dumped the canisters on it. There was a hiss of flame as each one went up and a lowering cloud of the dense grey smoke that had screened Monastery Hill swept

[178]

over the road junction, widening and thickening as new candles took fire, and drifting on the thin breeze to meet our advancing Allies.

When he got back to the truck Sergeant Transom took three small grenades from a cotton wool case, turned and hurled each to break tinkling on the fire.

"Tear gas bombs," he said. "What they gave us for the riots in Bougie—knew they'd come in handy."

The Kiwis and Yanks had by now seen each other across the plain, realized there was fresh rivalry for the Frascati and were both going flat out to be first to the junction. As we pulled away up the steep hill to Montepico, they disappeared, going neck and neck, into the smoke pall . . . the urgent cries of their commanders changed to yells of anguish . . . tires squealed . . . tracks screeched . . . metal clanged on metal . . . two brands of foul language roared through the smoke . . . but neither tank nor car appeared on the sunny side.

The Castello was bounded by mighty stone walls and we rolled through the triumphal gates and into the courtyard.

"Stone the crows!" said Private Drogue as we dismounted. "Bleeding A-rabs!"

The vast white vault was filled with figures in rust-brown burnouses. . . . The Goums had come down from the mountains, as ever, leading the field. . . . The Free French had beaten us to it . . . and by God! they were making remarkably free.

Enormous casks, twelve feet high, lined the walls. The face of each had been peppered with bullets . . . a dozen spouts of amber wine fountained from each of twenty tuns . . . the floor was a foot deep in vino and dead-drunk Moroccans . . . happy men paddled up and down in a grave African dance . . . others lay with smiling faces turned up to the wine shower. There was wine, wine, wine everywhere, but never a drop still portable.

[179]

"Gawd Strewth!" said Sergeant Transom. "We've had that Montepico '92. All this way and nothing to show for it."

"Cheer up, Sarge," said Private Spool. "At least you can get your feet drunk."

"That won't be the '92," I said. "It'll be locked away somewhere special. Let's search the place . . ."

We splashed through the wine-dark sea into the heart of the Castello. After hunting through a warren of crumbling corridors and cobwebbed rooms we finally found our prize . . . ten small barrels branded with 1892 over three interlaced crowns were stacked on the back doorstep together with a German officer's valise, a pile of laundry and a canteen of cutlery.

"Lovely grub!" crowed Sergeant Transom. "Jerry was going to cart it away but just didn't have the time. Them Goums did us a good turn after all . . ."

The men trundled the barrels across the courtyard.

"Load 'em all on the command truck. You'll all have to pack into the other truck till we get clear."

As we reached the gates of the Castello, a mixed column of Kiwis and Yanks came into sight cruising up the narrow road.

"We'll never get past those Shermans," I said. "We'll have to find another way down."

"It's the only way on our side," said the sergeant, driving through the gate and turning hard left into the gardens along the side of the wall. "If we lie low here, they'll belt into the courtyard and we can slip out behind for a clear run down."

We lined the trucks against the wall well-hidden by the trees and waited for the armour to come round the last bend. Suddenly the clatter of tracks was echoed from the other side of the courtyard . . . a German Tiger tank swung up to the back door.

"Everybody down!" yelled Sergeant Transom. "Jerry's sent back for his vino."

I dived to the floor as the Tiger swept the yard with its machineguns . . . bullets spanged into the wall . . . whining

[180]

over the top . . . swathing through the branches overhead . . . hammering on the armour of the half-track where it rose above the parapet. . . . I looked along at the other vehicles . . . both were down the slope and completely below the ramparts.

The Shermans opened up as they roared in through the gates . . . the Tiger backed out of the yard and disappeared from view . . . as the last Kiwi armoured car swept past us we drove out on to the road and went hell-for-leather down the hill.

At the road junction we passed a Polish motorcycle patrol escorting a watercart, followed hotly by a Canadian A.C.V. loaded with earthenware wine jars fit for the forty thieves. We drove hard for three-quarters of an hour across Kiwi land and stopped for the first time only when we were safely back in Musketeer territory.

"Oh! My Gawd!" groaned Sergeant Transom as he got down. . . . The tailboard of our half-track was dripping white wine and a torrent poured down when we opened it.

"That Tiger was firing A.P."

The top plates which had shown above the wall were cut by armour-piercing shot and a few neat bungholes were drilled in each barrel. Our bouncing at speed over the broken roads had tossed the casks higgledy-piggledy and their precious contents had drained away.

The second truck pulled up behind us ringing loud and tipsy as a Southend charabanc with a maudlin, bawling "Mother Machree." Sergeant Transom let down the back and two sections of Twelve Platoon tumbled out, each man carrying his private bottle and singing soulfully. . . . Private Drogue brought up the rear with a sack of bottles over his shoulder, flung up a vast salute and fell in a shambles at my feet.

Transom sniffed a bottle.

"Blimey! Brandy! Neat and best part of a pint each. What a bloody turn-up! The colonel'll strip the pair of us. No

Montepico '92, half the side out of a half-track, and the task force dead drunk to a man."

Surrounded by broken dreams, empty barrels, and sodden soldiers, I was inclined, at first thought, to join him in despair. But when I made a calm appreciation of the situation I saw there was still hope for my third pip.

"*Nil desperandum*, Sergeant," I said. "We can still win through. We may have lost the wine but we've still got the casks."

"Will the colonel be happy with empty barrels?"

"He might be if they were full . . . they've got the Montepico '92 mark on them. The right label makes all the difference to the wine. . . . We could plug the holes and fill them up again."

"What with? Just any old wine?"

"What have we got to lose?"

"Nothing, I suppose. But where are you going to get fifty gallons of wine from round here? Except for Montepico, the territory's drunk dry."

"Caesario," I said. "You get under cover here and sober this lot up. I'll be back as soon as I can."

The water cart driver was delighted to be back on a main highway and we made the hundred miles to Benevento in four hours. It was five in the evening when I knocked up Caesario and demanded, within the hour, two hundred litres of white wine.

"*Tenente*," he pleaded. "I give you plenty gin, plenty whisky, right away. But two hundred litres *vino bianca*, thata very difficult. The *Tedeschi* steala the wine, the *Inglesi*, *Americano*, drinka all the last vintage. . . . Maybe I collect you two hundred litres, some here, some there, but it won't be no good. . . ."

I took him round his contacts and we steadily topped up the water cart. We struck lucky at the last albergo, catching a job lot of seventy-five litres at one go.

"Thisa wine it madea for the poor, poor peoples, *tenente.* They put lotta apples and stuff with smalla grape and it makea very rough for the stomach." Caesario pursed up his lips like an aloe-taster and crouched in colic. "It makea plenty gripe for the bowel and I not like sell it for *Inglesi officiale.*"

Reflecting that beggars could not be connoisseurs, I paid him out and we were back with Sergeant Transom by midnight. He had made a beautiful job of repairing the bullet holes with knots of broom handle and a mixture of bostic and sawdust. We filled the casks from the water cart and set off at dawn with the second half-track full of grey lips and boozer's gloom.

The fervour of Colonel Plaster's welcome would have graced a French field marshal. He placed nine of the casks under armed guard and had the tenth mounted in the Intelligence tent. When he deemed it settled, he tapped it reverently.

"Will you have one, Goodbody? Just to celebrate your triumph."

"No thank you, Colonel," I said, recalling that seventy-five litres at the last albergo. "It would be wasted on me."

He drew three glasses and handed one each to Major Arkdust and Captain Tablet. They all drank expertly together, sniffing the bouquet, swilling their heads back and gnashing the liquid with their teeth. The colonel stroked the three branded crowns and smiled beatifically.

"Castello Montepico '92," he murmured. "The war has been worthwhile. . . . What panache! . . . What nobility of character! . . . What spirit! . . . The gun flint of a great Chablis . . . yet with the velvet nuance of a fine Sauterne . . ."

"Magnificent," said Major Arkdust. "Such eloquence! . . . Such marrow! . . . Silver-dry but full-bodied. . . . A masterpiece among wines!"

"Superb!" crooned Captain Tablet. "What finesse! A big

[183]

wine! Such heart! Such fragrance! It sings a truly wonderful song. . . ."

They sent five of the barrels home to the depot and Montepico '92 was solemnly drunk at each reunion. Until it ran out, regular attenders claimed that the searching effect of a Musketeers' reunion was equalled only by colonic lavage.

Chapter Fourteen

To me cricket is an English game that is designed for play on the village green, one boundary the pub and another the churchyard. . . . Cricket in India I found to be a very different affair in many respects. . . . One energized in blinding heat at an altitude of five thousand feet among the "dust Devils" that swept across the landscape at intervals, collapsing the sight-screens and necessitating temporary armistice while all hands prostrated themselves with head hand-covered to guard against asphyxiation.

SIR FREDERICK MORGAN
Peace and War—A soldier's Life

UNFORTUNATELY, THE TIMING of my Montepico triumph was not propitious. Although my star was in the ascendant, there were no vacant captaincies. Had but one of my seniors been efficient enough to obtain promotion or unlucky enough to have been written off during the ensuing three months, I am quite certain that I would have got that third pip. It was not till later that suitable vacancies arose and by that time I had suffered the misfortune of meeting my first Field Marshal.

After ten months slogging across the endless rivers of Italy, climbing and crawling and wading from Naples to Bologna, the Division was withdrawn to Egypt to rest, refit, and train reinforcements.

The Musketeers were living peacefully under canvas on the desert sands of Suez when the Field Marshal came to have lunch on the Regiment. He was on a four-day tour of the Division, visiting each unit in turn and coming to his climax with a monumental Inspection of Training.

The first thing the Army does when visited by a Field Marshal is to build him a private lavatory remote from the common suites. This is done, I believe, in the interests of morale, to protect the Wagnerian myth that the Higher Command are supermen without such ordinary human weaknesses, that they just do not do that sort of thing.

Colonel Plaster himself selected the site, the sanitary corporal fashioned a specially sandpapered single-seater, Captain Quartermaster Hollikin tested it for splinters with his own hands and personally supervised the erection of the hessian screen. The little temple of Cloaca was ready on the morning of the visit, and a path of whitewashed stones was laid to his entrance. All that remained was to protect its virginity until the Field Marshal arrived.

The adjutant sent for me.

"The colonel has ordered," he said, "that a guard be mounted over our visitor's private place. A duty of such delicacy can only be entrusted to an experienced officer. I have therefore selected you, as our senior subaltern, for the post of Field Marshal's Latrine Guard. You will be responsible for ensuring that his shrine is not desecrated before he arrives and that his privacy is protected should he venture inside."

I wore my pistol for the assignment, just in case there was trouble. If the rabble charged me, I would save the last round for the Field Marshal in protection of the Wagnerian legend. I patrolled round and round the hessian kiosk, occasionally glancing reverently over the top to ensure that no one had sneaked in behind my back and that snakes were not getting familiar on the woodwork. After our distinguished guest had been with us over three hours without coming out the back, I began to believe in the superman myth myself. I was mentally relieved when, at last, half an hour after lunch, he came out of the mess tent and strode urgently my way.

I came smartly to attention, stamping myself two inches down into the sand, and scything up a salute which vibrated like a tuning fork. He acknowledged hurriedly and went inside. The screen was in the French tradition, finishing about eighteen inches above ground and I could see his riding boots. I watched them until I judged that he had found his way all right and then looked firmly the other way. I may not be much on mess etiquette or getting women through revolving doors, but I do know how to behave as a Field Marshal's lavatory attendant.

When he came out I flung up another salute and the wind of its passing blew sand over the hessian. He stopped and studied me carefully from head to foot as if I had just stepped out of a flying saucer. Just to be on the safe side I held myself rigidly at the salute.

"What the hell are you here for?" he asked.

This had me for a minute. Captain Tablet had not told me what to do if spoken to. I sought frantically through my mind for a suitably servile reply.

"I am here, Field Marshal, sir," I finally said, "at your convenience."

The moment I said it I was sorry. I could have bitten my tongue off. I have never been a chap for the *double entendre*. All I had intended to indicate was that I was entirely at his service, to display the utmost in military humility.

Suspicion and lèse majesté stalked across his face and his eyes pierced mine like a pair of gimlets. He watched me for such a long time that I wondered if there might be a rare bird sitting on my head.

"Funny-cuts, eh?" he grunted at last, thrashed the innocent air with a what-the-hell backhander and marched off to the mess tent. Colonel Plaster was holding back the flap for him, and as he stepped through the Field Marshal spoke a few decisive words to my commander. Together they turned and took another long slow gander at me, which plainly did nothing to further my career.

A gigantic divisional charade was laid on for the Field Marshal's Inspection of Training next day. The division was spread out down to every last platoon, troop, and section over

[187]

some two hundred square miles of wilderness, each group demonstrating within its own plot a particular phase of training—gunners gunning, signallers signalling, cooks cooking, and engineers engineering.

Each platoon of the Musketeers was detailed to depict in action a different aspect of our martial role. Nine Platoon did Battle Drills, Ten Platoon displayed Consolidation on the Objective, Eleven Platoon enacted Unarmed Combat, and Twelve Platoon was called up to demonstrate, on Plot F27, Recreational Training—Cricket.

The individual plots were allocated by Divisional Headquarters from the map and were ingeniously laid out in a tight-fitting mosaic so that the Field Marshal would not have to walk more than fifty yards from the road to see any of the tableaux. I would have joined vociferously in the applause for this splendid piece of staff work if F27 had not turned out to be three and a half acres of corrugated rock. It was the original field ready-made for Jason, sown with dragon's teeth, and surfaced with millions of tiny, white tombstones.

After inspecting the pitch with Sergeant Transom I went to see the brigade major in charge of F Sector.

"We can't play cricket on that," I said. "There isn't a blade of grass or a flat foot of soil on the whole area."

"You've got to," he replied. "F27 you've been allotted and that's where the Field Marshal will expect to see Recreational Training—Cricket. So get on with it."

We finally selected for the wicket a green strip where a varnish of moss covered the rippling granite beneath.

"Good job the stumps are in wooden blocks," said Sergeant Transom, "or we'd need dynamite to get them in."

Lest the Musketeers be criticized for waste of manpower, I was allowed only thirteen men for the fixture, a force which was completely employed by two men batting and eleven fielding among the boulders. The Field Marshal was timed to arrive with us at 11.45 hours, and, so that all would be swinging by then, F Sector started training at 11.00 hours.

We opened the bowling with Corporal Hink, medium pace, right arm over. He normally delivered amiable up-and-down stuff, but on our rock-candy mountain he came off the pitch like Larwood with a liver on. It was like playing cricket on the Giant's Causeway. The first ball reared up six feet above the batsman's head, the second took the cap off the wicket-keeper, the third broke on a Jurassic fault and went straight to the stomach of mid-off, the fourth leapt clear out of F27 and laid low the key man of a bridging party in F29. The batsman hit the fifth in self-defence, and the ball went off like a demented jackrabbit, ricocheting from crag to crag until it struck an outcrop of quartz and broke into four pieces. At which point Sergeant Transom called Over.

Private Drogue came on at the other end and turned out a natural Trueman. His first ball was heard to pitch but was never seen again until it smashed the windscreen of an ambulance performing at the A.D.S. in E14 and laid out the driver. Although the R.A.M.C. were at first rather upset about the windscreen, they were finally grateful for the provision of a real casualty in place of their dummy.

The second ball kept low, hit the terrified bat and zoomed away like a horizontal rocket, zig-zagging from col to col, and fieldsmen going down like redskins to get out of the way. The third got up after a sputnik, bounced once on the road and took the brigade major in the small of the back. I called a halt and told Sergeant Transom to put on two other bowlers.

"I can't," he said. "They're the only ones in the party that can bowl overarm."

I went over to discuss the situation with the brigade major and to ask him for our ball back. He gave his decision that in no circumstances could a Field Marshal be shown Army cricketers bowling underarm.

"Get back there at once and keep on playing. He's due here any minute now."

We shifted the line of the wicket so that Drogue's sky-scrapers would be cut off by a small, uninhabited mountain

[189]

and restricted both bowlers to a three-pace run-up. The sun blazed down on our rock-bound plain and our feet were slowly roasting alive in their gym shoes. It was bruising for the batsmen who just had to stand and take any bodyline that was coming to them; one false evasive step into the dragon's teeth and they'd lost another ankle. The fieldsmen stumbled in misery across the baking tombstones, wrenching insteps, stubbing toes, and living in mortal fear of a Drogue rebound.

By 12.30 hours the Field Marshal had still not arrived, two more balls had been ground to fragments and we all had feet like fire-walkers. Footsore, weary, and dripping perspiration, we plodded on like characters in some Greek cricketing tragedy, doomed by the gods to play out eternity on the stony purgatory of F27.

At 13.10 hours we were down to our last ball, and that was breaking up fast. A Hink delivery turned through two right angles and the ball came back to him cube-shaped. I took it over to show the brigade major. He was fraying badly and had bitten his nails down to the cuticle. His wireless had broken and nobody knew where the Field Marshal was.

"For God's sake, go on playing, man," he said. "He may turn up any second."

I asked him what we should do if our last ball broke up and he said to carry on going through the motions.

"Shadow cricket?" said Sergeant Transom when I passed on the order. "The men'll never stand for it. They'll think they've gone barmy. We'll just have to make this one last out."

I made a quick appreciation of the situation and realized that the essential thing was to stop the ball hitting the rocks. I rapidly devised a form of cricket to this end. All the fieldsmen gathered in a close ring about the wicket while Corporal Hink and Private Drogue, unchanged for three and a quarter hours, hobbled up on braised feet and bowled slow full tosses so that the batsmen could play spoon-shots direct to the fieldsmen. After a little practice, we got the hang of this ladies' pat-a-cake and still had our ball intact when, at 13.50 hours, the Field Marshal arrived.

He gave me that long, slow look and his eyes narrowed suddenly in the displeasure of recognition. I stamped stiffly to attention on feet of liquid fire. He watched in silence while Private Drogue ladled up an over of donkey-drops which the batsman patted gingerly away. After Corporal Hink had followed with six lollipops tossed up from a static position, the Field Marshal turned to me.

"Bloody rotten bowlers you've got," he said and stalked straight back to his car. As it disappeared in a wake of white dust my whole cricketing contingent subsided to the ground. The gridiron of stone teeth mortified the flesh like a bed of nails, but no pain was important if the weight was off the feet. The brigade major pranced around in agitation lest the All-Highest should return but we were past caring about his career. We lay on the field of battle with steam-puffing toes until the torture of the tiny tombstones drove us off.

Major Arkdust came out of his tent to meet us as I led my crippled team back to their pavilion.

"What the hell's the matter with your lot, Goodbody?" he demanded. "I thought you were on a cushy game of cricket."

"We was," muttered Private Drogue. "Cricket on the red-hot cobbles of hell."

"The wicket, sir," I said stoically, "was rather lively. I am afraid that when I have completed my foot inspection there will be a large number of men to be excused boots and . . ."

"There will not. . . . Our little holiday's over. They've got a full-scale revolution in Greece and the advance parties leave in the morning."

"But my feet, sir!" pleaded Corporal Hink. "I've got blisters like barrage ballons."

"Not to worry," said Major Arkdust blithely, "rebels rarely have boots on. You'll be able to fight them barefoot . . ."

[191]

Chapter Fifteen

... Thus, in the tragic case of Greece, where British soldiers, despite
an outspoken protest on the part of the British people, cold-bloodedly
shot down Greek anti-fascists ...

ELLIOTT ROOSEVELT
As He Saw It

It is odd ... now that some years have past, to see how completely the
policy for which I and my colleagues fought so stubbornly has been
justified by events. ... I saw quite plainly that Communism would be
the peril civilization would have to face after the defeat of Nazism and
Fascism.

SIR WINSTON CHURCHILL
The Second World War

It is the West that forces us to fight to the last. However it will
transpire that the winner will not be the West but the East.

ADOLF HITLER TO HIS GENERALS, 11TH DECEMBER 1944

THE POSITION WAS SERIOUS when we landed in Greece in
December 1944. The Allied Forces in Europe held the
Grande Bretagne Hotel and its environs in the centre of
Athens and enjoyed the occasional use of the airport. The
ELAS rebels held the rest of Greece. Colonel Plaster called a
Montgomery-meeting of all officers and N.C.O.'s to drive
home the full gravity of our situation.

"... supplies are very difficult. All our dumps were located
on the outskirts of Athens and the blasted rebels have got the

lot. The N.A.A.F.I. warehouse held two hundred gross of whisky, three hundred of gin, and God only knows how much beer. It is rumoured that the first United Nations relief consignment contained twelve hundred bottles of bourbon. Intelligence believe that at R.A.F. Headquarters there was a secret Mosquito with its reserve tanks full of brandy. . . . And now everything is lost . . . all supplies have been cut off." He spread his arms in naked despair. "But we must not give in. We must grind back these ragtag and bobtail fellers as we ground back the Boche. I look to the Musketeers to be in the forefront of the battle and to recapture as rapidly as possible the vital supply dumps upon which depend the success or failure of any campaign. . . . The only stock at present held by the Allies consists entirely of the local wine, retsina, which tastes strongly of pine disinfectant . . ." He pursed his lips and shivered delicately at the memory. "The flavour comes from the pine resin which is smeared inside the barrels before the wine is put in. When the Turks conquered Greece they tried to discourage the national pastime of drunkenness by ordaining that the wine should be made unpalatable by adulterating it with pine resin. But our ancient and gallant ally, the Greek, defied this atrocity of his teetotal oppressors. They applied themselves to this coniferous brew, they proudly persevered over the years, and finally succeeded in developing a taste for wine with pine resin in it. . . . What the Greeks can do, the British can do. It will be hard at first but we must keep trying. Until our efforts are blessed by the Lord Mighty in Battle with success and the recapture of the hard stuff, we must emulate the Greeks and acquire a taste for retsina. . . . And may God be with us all!"

With the reinforcements of the Division, it was the plan steadily to expand our perimeter until the enemy was pushed out of Athens, and to combine this process with special sorties into the suburbs to relieve beleaguered places of importance. During our initial week of skirmishing around the

[193]

West End, Major Arkdust returned beaming from a conference at R.H.Q.

"C Company, with under command one phalanx of the Greek National Guard, is to make a sortie directed on the district of Coralos, twelve miles out. We will be allocated armoured trucks for transport and since the enemy have no A.P. weapons or artillery, life should not be overly difficult. We will split into three columns, one under Captain Croker directed on the waterworks, one under Lieutenant Goodbody to relieve the 812th General Hospital, and one, commanded by myself, will recapture the Herodias Brewery."

From the detail of his orders I learnt that the 812th General Hospital had been cut off since the first day of the rising six weeks before. It was assumed that I would find that the building which housed it had been sacked and the fifty nursing sisters had suffered fates worse than death.

". . . and now," said Major Arkdust at the end. "Any questions?"

"Yes, sir," I said. "Could I have a map of Athens?"

"Very sorry, Goodbody, but we've still only one map per company. Platoons will have to make do with the tramways guide for a bit longer. You can't go wrong for Coralos if you start at Omonia Square and follow the No. 7 route. The line finishes at the Coralos depot."

I took my task back to the platoon and gave out my own battleplan.

"Nurses, eh?" said Corporal Dooley. "Ought to be a bit of all right when we get there."

"Those poor girls, Corporal Dooley," I said, "will have been through six weeks of pure hell. It is up to us when we get there to behave like English gentlemen."

"Nobody won't be there, sir Lieutenant," said Spiros, my interpreter, a gloomy, thirty-year-old monarchist moulded on Mickey Rooney. "Them ELAS bastards take the women to the mountains and burn down the hospital. You see. I know for these things. I know Greek peoples."

[194]

My Anglo-Greek column formed up at dawn by the No. 7 tram stop in Omonia Square. As we drove out towards our perimeter, machine guns started to rattle on street corners and the day's warfare began. I watched the lamp posts anxiously for No. 7 tram stops, and we went well for the two miles to the borderline. There was a brisk skirmish going on over the final crossroads. On our side, two hidden Brens chattered red streaks of tracer from the fire-blackened shell of a police station, and rifle fire crackled back across the square from the shops opposite.

"That'll be the para-boys," said Corporal Doolcy.

"How do you know?" I asked. There was nobody in view.

"That's a jeweller's shop. The para-boys fight their revolution from jeweller's shop to jeweller's shop. Some of them got that many rings they can't bend their fingers."

A red-bereted paratroop sergeant crept out of the police station behind the screen of my armoured truck.

"Where are you heading?"

"Coralos."

"Best of luck. We'll ease up while you go through." He ran back and a few moments later the firing from our side died away. But the Greek bullets swept unabated across the square. Although we were armoured I saw no point in risking a stray one through a slit or a shot-up tire at this stage and waited back between the cover of the corner buildings.

Spiros stood up and yelled a long protest in Greek. An answering voice came back from the enemy and after a bellowing conversation their firing ceased and all was silent at the crossroads.

"What did you say to them, Spiros?"

"I say we're not interested in their battle. We got to go and fight some other place. We don't want no jewellery out of their shop. Sooner they let us get on our way sooner they can get on with their battle."

Carefully spaced at fifteen vehicles to the mile and travelling precisely at the official speed of fifteen miles in the hour,

[195]

my column of twelve trucks rolled majestically over the cross-roads.

"Thank you very much," I cried politely to the paratroops.

"*Efaristo!*" shouted Spiros to his countrymen.

The No. 7 tram certainly took a tortuous route thereafter and I had to be extremely alert to catch its convolutions.

"Strewth!" said Gripweed, who was driving, after twenty minutes of twisting and turning. "I'm getting dizzy. If we turn left once more we're going to be treading on our own tail."

He wasn't quite right, but after two more turnings we found ourselves cruising back the way we had come to the jeweller's shop junction. The battle was waging hot and strong again, but as we came into sight, the firing slowly faded away and my convoy sailed solemnly back over the crossroads.

"Blimey," said the paratroop sergeant. "But you've been quick."

"So sorry to interrupt you again," I said. "But we seem to have taken the wrong turning."

A derisive Grecian voice boomed out of the jeweller's best bedroom. Spiros cat-called in reply.

"Bloody damn cheek!" he said. "He say why we come running back to Winston Churchill so soon. We see bogeyman or boy with popgun?"

I stopped and studied the tramway guide.

"If we turn right here and then right again," I decided, "we can pick up the No. 7 route without passing that cross-roads again."

Gripweed followed my directions and sure enough we picked up the No. 7 signs and proceeded on our complicated way.

"Oh, Gawd stone me gently!" he said ten minutes later. "We're coming up to Mary's house again."

Impossibly, we were bearing down on the crossroads once again, coming this time down the northern arm, at least from a direction we had not used before. The gun fire trickled once more to silence as I led my parade rumbling across the square. The paratroop sergeant began swearing most unpleasantly as we went by and I can only assume that he had not noticed my rank. I leaned out to mollify him.

"I really am most awfully sorry, Sergeant, to break into things again. There must be something wrong with my map."

"Get out of it," he yelled. "Get off up to Coralos and leave us alone."

Greek jeers came out of the jeweller's and Spiros spat in a silent disdain.

"Funny bastard over there. We trying to make out we a big army, he ask, by driving round and round like on stage? We don't fool him, he say. He recognize us every time."

I held a study group with Spiros over the tramways guide. Unfortunately he didn't know this neck of Athens, and the map only showed main streets. But he worked out a route off to the left which would get us back to No. 7 without interfering with the warfare up the road.

It worked beautifully and we picked up the tram signs again and were well on the way to Coralos when Gripweed began to laugh hysterically.

"Oh! No! It can't be? We must be on the ancient Greek Inner Circle or something. . . ."

We came round a hairpin bend and on to the crossroads again, this time from the south. The crossfire tailed away rather grudgingly as I urged Gripweed to spurt across, thus keeping the interruption to the minimum.

"Please accept my sincerest apologies," I cried as we passed the paratroops, "but this interruption is caused by circumstances quite beyond my control."

The sergeant was dancing up and down in the doorway of the police station and hurling stones at my trucks as they went by.

"You come round here again, we'll bloody do the lot of

you! We'll teach you to take the mickey out of the air-borne. . . . We got a war on here. We ain't got time for your blasted ring-o'-roses . . ."

Equal fury bawled out from the ELAS.

"He say what the hell we trying now," said Spiros. "The psychological warfare? Are we trying to drive him god-blasted mad by going round and round in circles? He say if he gets his hands on you, sir Lieutenant, he personally castrate you."

I stopped the column and Sergeant Transom, who was travelling with the National Guard, came up.

"I'm on to their game now, sir," he said. "There's a couple of kids keep switching the tram signs about on the lamp posts. I caught sight of them last time round."

"How diabolical," I said. "The indoctrination of chil-dren."

"I don't know about any indoctrination. They were killing themselves laughing last time we went by. . . . But we're going to be all right now, ain't we, Aristotle."

With him had come a round, beaming National Guard in a greatcoat three sizes too large and a cap, in the same ratio, too small.

"O.K. boss. All hunky-dory. Coralos, right away! Ding, ding!"

He pulled the string of an imaginary tram bell.

"You speak bloody Greek," said Spiros to him, half-draw-ing his revolver. "I'm the interpreter round here."

Aristotle was a No. 7 tram driver in civilian life. The only way to Coralos, he announced, was back over the crossroads and straight on. The battle for the jeweller's shop had settled down again and volleys were spanging back and forth across the square. I turned the column and once more we advanced on our objective. As we reached the junction, the firing politely died for a few moments. Then, just as we were in the middle of the crossroads, the paratroops stood up in the shell of the police station, the ELAS came to the windows of their shop and both sides, their true enmity sadly forgotten, turned

[198]

their combined fire towards us. As the bullets whined over the top of the truck and Anglo-Greek imprecations echoed against the armour, Gripweed put his foot down and we ran through the international gauntlet and out on our mission of mercy up the Coralos road.

Once out of the range of both friend and foe we bowled steadily along under Aristotle's guidance. We were hindered on our way by roadblocks built French-fashion of cobbles and carts, old men dropping petrol bombs from third-floor balconies, blackbearded priests with grenades in their cassocks, and the young lady captured in Kalamaki a week before with a gun up her skirt. We weren't actually attacked by any damsels so intimately armed, but the official report of the young lady of Kalamaki was taken as licence by Corporal Dooley and others to lift the skirts of any presentable woman we encountered just to make sure. Except at the roadblocks, where we had to drive off small defence parties, the main ELAS forces, probably disliking the weight of my column, confined their efforts to attack by incendiary-tram.

We met the first of these secret weapons when we were about three miles from Coralos.

"Good Gawd Almighty!" yelled Gripweed. "Everybody up the curb!"

He spun the wheel hard over, mounted the pavement and drove into an undertaker's window. . . . Two hundred yards ahead, thundering down the hill, came a riderless tram . . . flames roaring back from its windows, smoke belching over the roof, and exploding ammunition spitting red and yellow fireworks out of its flanks . . . bucking and rearing over the track, wheels screeching on the bends, the fiery juggernaut hurtled past just as the tail of my column followed Gripweed on to the sidewalk and gave it right of way. Four hundred yards farther on it leapt a hump-bridge, ski-jumped for five incredible seconds . . . lost its balance and crashed broadside into the Dionysos Kinema.

"I've been attacked by some weapons in my time," said

[199]

Sergeant Transom as we crouched behind the coffin lids. "Back in Jellybad they used to bombard us with bags of boiling hot camel-dung. But this is the first time anybody ever came at me with a tram . . . and look out! Here comes another!"

Down roared a second flame-monster, exploding bodily a furlong away, leaving the track and skidding wheels first towards us, mowing down lamp standards like matchsticks till it came finally to rest three light-lengths ahead.

"Someone must have been to school in England," I said. "They got this idea from Drake and his fire-ships."

"Or from Blackpool and their illuminated trams," said Gripweed.

"How many trams have they got up there?" asked Sergeant Transom.

"Must be about a hundred," said Spiros. "It's a main depot at Coralos. And they've got loads of tar barrels from the new road-works."

"They could keep us out all day with that lot. . . . Heads down, lads!"

The third tram-incendiary was better balanced and flashed flaming past us, over the hump-bridge and on out of sight. The next couple came off the rails on the down run and finished as burning hulks among the shaven lamp standards. Aristotle the tram driver was sobbing quietly at the sight of his beautiful street-galleys crashing down to their fiery death and talking through his tears to Spiros.

"I ask him," explained the interpreter, "if there's another way up to Coralos. He say no, we got to go up this hill for one mile. Then we come to crossroads and can go rest of way off the tram route."

"Do other tram routes join at the crossroads?" asked Sergeant Transom.

"Yes."

"Good. Then maybe we can get past these flaming dreadnoughts, after all. . . . Get two sections out, Corporal Dooley. Bring the truck tools and a crowbar. We're patrolling with Aristotle up to the crossroads."

We fired everything we had at longest range just to keep any ELAS around on the jump and made it to the crossroads without trouble.

"Hunky-dory," said Aristotle. "Here she is. O. K., boss. Right away . . . ding, ding!"

He levered the crowbar down into the slit in the pavement and heaved the points over. Sergeant Transom hammered in a rock to wedge the lines and jumped back as the next flame-wagon came hurtling down. . . . It swung with the points away from our road and went hurtling on down the left-hand fork and out of sight round the bend below.

"Operation Tram-Diversion complete, sir," reported Sergent Transom.

"Well done, indeed." I pointed down the new route for the public transport volcanoes. "And where will that road take them, Spiros?"

He spoke to Aristotle.

"Ain't nobody but ELAS down there, sir Lieutenant. That road runs straight down past the waterworks and the Herodias Brewery."

I consoled myself with the thought that both Major Arkdust and Captain Croker were paid more money than I was. As we advanced again the roadblocks became thicker and the opposition heavier. Through the hot, dusty afternoon we skirmished and scuffled from street corner to street corner, quelling some pockets of resistance by simple weight of mortar and machine gun firepower, defeating others more determined by my classical left hook outflanking technique. What with those paratroops, the V trams, and the stress of active command, it was a long, hard day, but I was sustained throughout by the image of those fifty grateful nurses fluttering about me as I bounded into the hospital to release them from six weeks of hell. The ELAS made their final stand at the entrance to the square in which the 812th General Hospital stood, and I had to mount a set-piece assault to hit them for six out of Coralos. After an hour's fighting for the strategic public lavatories, they finally broke up and pulled out.

Drawing my revolver, I ran up the steps and into the reception hall. Everything was quiet, polished and orderly, and nurses walked primly to and fro. Nobody took any notice of me. There was a door marked "Matron." Revolver at the heroic ready, tin hat at a devil-may-care angle, I burst triumphantly in.

"It's all over!" I cried. "The 812th General Hospital is relieved!"

Matron, handsome and gold-gray, looked up from her writing.

"Good evening," she said.

"Good evening," I said. "You're all liberated!"

"Liberated? From whom?"

"From the rebels. The ELAS and the Communists and all that. Are there any left in the building?" I dropped into a fighting crouch.

"In the building?" She was horrified at the idea. "In *my* hospital? . . . I should think not. Except for a few of their wounded. They came swarming in about six weeks ago but I told them I can't have armed men about my hospital. I'll take your wounded, I said, but the rest of you must get out." She waved her hand majestically. "And they went. They argued at first but I soon sent them packing. . . . And tell me, Lieutenant, was that you and your men making all that noise in the square just now?"

"Yes," I said. "It was. We were fighting the ELAS. Quelling the revolution . . . you know . . ."

"That's as it may be but there are sick people in here and I can't have all that noise going on outside my windows. And

[202]

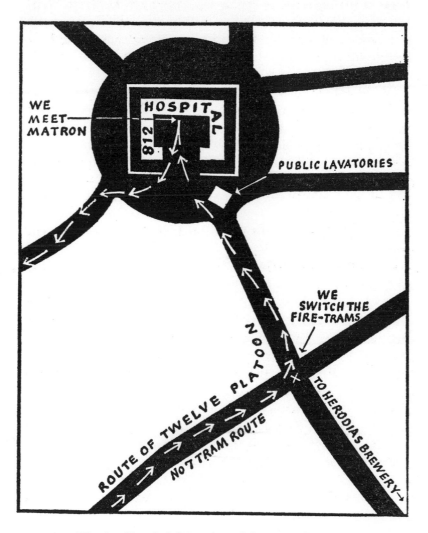

The 812 Hospital Campaign—Advance and Retreat

you'll have to move that armoured car out of the courtyard. I wouldn't let the ELAS bring arms into the hospital and I can't let you. If you let me know how many men you've got I'll send you a hot meal down to the gates. . . . God bless my soul!" She stopped and pointed aghast at my ammunition boots. "Did you come across my hall in those dreadful boots?"

"I'm sorry . . . I'm afraid I did . . ."

She stood up. Fearful she would devour me, I fell back a step.

"Keep still!" she commanded. "Don't make it worse. Those great hobnails! Across my polished floors! Whatever next?"

I froze on the spot while she sent for an orderly and two slipmats. She put one under each of my feet and I had to shuffle miserably back to the front door like a duck on ice. The crew thought I was crazy when I made them push the truck out of the courtyard lest the noise of the engine bring her out.

We withdrew to the far side of the square and that night I sent Spiros to get a message through to the local ELAS commander suggesting he might like to start fighting tomorrow in some other street. He sent back to say he was only too pleased—he'd already had a basinful of Matron himself.

Chapter Sixteen

Our concern over these affairs illustrates forcibly the old truism that political considerations can never wholly be separated from military ones and that war is a mere continuation of political policy in the field of force.

GEN. DWIGHT D. EISENHOWER
Crusade in Europe

THE MUSKETEERS CONTINUED throughout the Greek Campaign as motorized infantry, driving steadily northwards, and when an uneasy truce was agreed after six weeks' fighting, we found our progress halted some fifty miles from Athens. A truce line was drawn across the country at the limit of the Allied advance. The agreement stipulated that the ELAS troops should withdraw unmolested beyond this line and that hostilities should be temporarily suspended while attempts were made to obtain peace by negotiation.

We were spread very thinly on the ground and Twelve Platoon, strengthened by a few National Guard—Goodbody-Force as I called it in my reports—occupied the town of Dolia. The truce wasn't really popular round there, and up in the mountains, just across the road, thousands of ELAS warriors were restively withdrawn, trigger-fingers itching and anxious for any pretext to be over the line and at me and my hopeful half-hundred holding the town.

Dolia had been pretty well stripped by the Germans when they retreated and there was no local government to notice.

Inured by occupation to regard the latest military commander as the source of all authority, the town automatically transferred responsibility for its administration to me. And thus gave me my first experience of the soldier in politics.

Things were very niggly on the nerves. The only telephone line still working connected to the ELAS headquarters over the border and the local editor would ring them nightly for news. A Swede from the Red Cross came back from his relief tours of the mountains with daily and ever-gloomier forebodings.

"Dere are more and more of dem all around you every day. Dey sharpen up deir weapons, dey practise with deir guns. Tonight, it is for sure dey come down to attack you. Tonight, it is dey come to cut everybody's throats."

Every night, according to his intelligence, was to be the night of the long knives and the continual evening stand-to's gave me little time for my Memoirs and brought serious complaints from the lady who owned the town brothel. As I have already explained, I am not a chap for that sort of thing myself, but as a military commander one cannot close one's eyes to the fact that such places exist and that, let's face it, soldiers are wont to frequent them. I apologize to any lady readers for mentioning such establishments and would assure them that war, unfortunately, is like that.

Madame was a brisk, efficient business woman who came straight to the point.

"Why you wanna ruin my business, Captain? Why you wanna make me poor woman? Why for you make the soldiers come out of my house eight, nine, ten o'clock every night?"

"I have no desire to reduce your turnover, madame. It is vital for security reasons that I have the soldiers back in their billets at recognized times."

I did not bother to correct her misinterpretation of my rank. It was all in the interests of local prestige. And perhaps, coming from a Greek, it was a favourable omen—the Delphic oracle and all that.

"Why for you got to have them in billets before even children go to bed?"

"Because we may be attacked at any time by the ELAS. I must have my troops available in their billets to defend the town and carry out my orders."

"You not get attacked by ELAS. Not yet. My piano player, Iliou, got a brother, Tasos, who's big shot over in ELAS. So you don't have to worry. I tell you when Iliou say ELAS going to attack."

"I'm afraid, madame," I said, smiling deprecatingly, "that you do not appreciate the methods of British Army Intelligence. We could never base our defence arrangements on the reports of a man who plays the piano in a brothel."

She shook her head in puzzlement.

"But if you are attacked, why you want them back in billets? Their billets are scattered all over town."

"The section billets, madame, have been carefully sited so that each forms a strong point in my Dolia Defense System."

"You can't defend the whole town with fifty-six men, Captain! You want to know the best strong point in Dolia? You want to know where the Germans had their machine guns?"

"Where?"

"On the roof of my brothel. My house stand up on the hill. From my roof you can shoot anybody, anywhere in Dolia. My brothel best damned strong point in all Dolia. Look, I show you on map . . ."

And after I'd studied my map for a while under her German-trained direction, I began to feel she was quite right.

"So you do better, Captain," she said, "to let your soldiers stay all night in my brothel and not go back to billets at all. Then if ELAS attack you know just where they are."

"Much as I appreciate your tactical theories, madame, I'm afraid that Allied Forces Headquarters would not approve of my entire garrison sleeping every night in your brothel."

"Why not? When the Italians were here they used to sleep all night with my girls."

"We are not Italians, madame. It is a matter of traditional British morality. Lady Astor would have me up at the bar of the House if I allowed such a thing. I cannot officially encourage soldiers to spend the night at your brothel."

"But it's safer for your soldiers that way. My girls good, clean girls inspected by doctor every Monday. You make your men stay all night in billets they get sleeping with amateurs . . ." Her face filled with hatred at the mention. "Dirty, little amateurs . . . they never get inspected. They give all your soldiers terrible diseases . . ."

"Even so, madame, and giving all due weight to your point of hygiene, I cannot authorize them to sleep at your brothel."

She thought for a moment. Then inspiration came.

"All right then, Captain. Soldiers can't stay sleep with the girls at my place like Italians. Then you do like the Germans did. You let soldiers take my girls back with them to their billets for the night."

She clapped her hands in jubilation.

"I'm sorry," I said, "but Lady Astor and the Chaplain General wouldn't stand for that either. The British Army would never officially sanction the overnight stay of prostitutes in official billets."

She sighed enormously and her eyes asked heaven for patience. Then she squared herself up and settled to the attack like a female D. A.

"Now, Captain! You agree that my house is very fine for defence?"

"Yes, but . . ."

"And if your soldiers are there they are in good place to fight?"

"Well, yes . . ."

"And that my girls are cleaner for soldiers then bloody amateurs in billets?"

"That may be so . . ."

"Then why not you let my girls and your soldiers be happy all night together?"

[208]

"Because . . . because . . . because it just isn't done."

She threw up her hands and asked God to look after me.

"It . . . just . . . is . . . not . . . done!" She beat out the words in fury with the flat of her fist. "The Italians . . . they are sensible people. . . . The Germans . . . you can reason with them. . . But, my God! . . . *The English!*" Her voice rose to a frustrated wail of international despair and she swept out of the office.

I was tempted to put a machine gun section up on her roof, but I couldn't think of anyone I could trust. So I contented myself for the time being with putting a tail on Iliou the piano player.

The two main political thorns in my flesh were Agro and Spiliou, two dark, flint-eyed little men who ran the local Communist Party office at 27 High Street, Dolia. They were dedicated to provoking the bloodthirsty British into acts of tyranny which could be boiled up into a pretext for breaking the truce. We were under pain-of-death orders to be all sweetness and light to the local populace and, in any case, were not anxious to see the Swedish prophecies fulfilled.

At first they organized parades with Union Jack-covered coffins round and round our headquarters, painted on walls rude things in Greek about Winston Churchill and held *à-bas-les-Anglais* meetings each evening in the main square. It depressed them profoundly when they found that we watched these entertainments with beaming benignity and they gave them up altogether when unidentified burglars got into their offices one night and stole their coffins, flags, paint, brushes, and rabble-rousing megaphones.

Having decided there was no future in trying to goad us to acts of violence in moments of passion, Agro and Spiliou settled down to a cold war of attrition in which their main tactic was eternal deputation. Every morning, sharp at nine, there would be an aggrieved organization waiting on my official doorstep. It is a point of honour in Greek deputations that every member must have his individual spiel. With a people whose stamina for the discussion of political science is rivalled only by their ineptitude in its application, these individual orations totalled up to a long time. It rarely took less than an hour for a complete deputation to deliver its impassioned complaints and for me to make my diplomatic, peace-loving replies. And as each delegation departed, another would be waiting to take its place—the Municipal Washhouses and Street Cleaning Committee asking why the British didn't issue free brooms as the Germans did, followed by the Amalgamated Metal Beaters Union complaining they had no metal to beat, the Young Wives Fellowship dissatisfied with the quality of the free powdered milk and their consequent difficulty in selling it on the black market, the National Society of Waiters and Café Assistants demanding we provide more fuel to run the electricity supply all night, the League of Socialist Youth exhibiting a fully-paid-up comrade whose head had been shaved and stained bright blue by the Royalists, and God-appealing officials of the Mothers Union of Attica displaying sundry beautiful daughters whom they claimed the British had lately liberated from the burden of virginity.

Although the members before me changed as deputation succeeded deputation, the two constants were Agro and Spiliou. They ushered in each party, ticking them off in their little black books, and were ever present at the back, listening discreetly for the party line and ensuring that the orators fulfilled their allotted spans. Their idea, clearly, was to keep wheeling up petitioners until finally my patience would become exhausted and I would reject a legitimate grievance, kick a party bodily down the stairs, refuse point-blank to see any more delegations, or perform some similar act of violence which would reveal the British as the Fascist Jackals, Reactionary Hyenas, and Imperialist Vampires they really were.

I had Sergeant Transom with me when I received the delegations. I thought that a committee of two would display the democracy of the British in action and protect me from any charges of trying to impose a dictatorship in Dolia. Experience of political negotiation would also help him, I felt, in his development into potential officer material. At first, we both listened to our voluble visitors with the patience of Job and the benevolence of Pickwick. For the first day of continual embassy our tolerance held out well and we were still smiling fixedly at the end; on the second day the golden Greek voices grated on our ears like a rust-ridden rookery and we grew short of breath in the garlic-sprayed atmosphere; and by the close of the third, Agro and Spiliou were well on the way to victory. Our paternal smirks had faded into rat trap scrowls. Simon Legree was our paragon and we quiet saw Hitler's point of view.

It was in the middle of the fourth morning that Sergeant Transom finally cracked. As the committee of the Hellenic Society of Master Bakers and Pastrycooks retired after demanding for seventy minutes that icing sugar be given priority on all British convoys, he slammed down his pencil and swore unbrokenly for a minute and a half.

". . . and if those two blue-chinned, shifty-eyed bastards bring one more delegation through that door I'll take the pair of them by the scruff of their necks and toss them out the flaming window!"

In my heart I agreed with him, but as an officer and local military commander I could not, of course, afford to lose my self-control.

"Steady, Sergeant," I said. "We mustn't crack up now. One outburst of violence on our side and the truce may be broken. Peace in Greece in our time rests upon our shoulders."

"Maybe they don't want peace in Greece. They've never had none for the last forty years. One more afternoon like yesterday and they'll be making up my bed in Banstead."

[211]

"And I'll be needing a new larynx," said Spiros, hoarse and broken-voiced as a prairie bishop.

The next delegation was already being shepherded in by Agro and Spiliou.

"Chin up, chaps," I whispered. "Never do to show weakness in front of the enemy."

Sergeant Transom sat muttering direfully to himself as the Ancient Order of Olive Pressers dilated upon the damage British bullets had done to the olive crop, the familiarity of Private Drogue with a female operator bending over her press, and the depression of their exorbitant local profits by the dumping on Dolia of Royalist olive oil from the hinterland. They demanded, after fifty minutes of over-articulation, that a military edict should be issued forbidding anyone from outside the town to sell olive oil in Dolia.

"Eager as His Majesty's Government are to do all in their power to assist the Dolia Branch of the Ancient Order of Olive Pressers," I said, "and much as they deprecate the sexual liberties taken with one of its loyal lady members by Private Drogue, I am afraid that they could not be party to an economic arrangement of the nature you suggest. It would be grossly unfair to the people of the surrounding villages. If they do not sell their oil in the market at Dolia, where can they sell it? It would be against all British principles of fair play to bar the villagers in order to keep your prices up. That sort of thing just wouldn't be playing the game. It simply isn't cricket."

A gentle inquiring silence came over them. They looked wonderingly at one another.

"Crick-et," someone tinkled in two syllables.

"Cricket," everybody muttered, clicking the word like castanets. "Crick-et . . . crick-et."

Perhaps it stirred a faint bell in the Dolian memory; once, maybe, a commercial traveller had come into the tavern and told them about the cricketers of Corfu.

"Crick-et," said a nubile olive presser in a sky-blue dress. "What, please, is the crick-et?"

I saw a chance to come off the defensive and switch to the attack. I was in there sharp as Portia and paying them out in their own money.

"Cricket," I said, "is an English game played between two teams of eleven players. It is played on a cricket-pitch which is twenty-two yards in length. Three stumps, twenty-eight inches high and set nine inches apart are placed at either end. Each set of stumps is called a wicket. Cricket is played with a bat and ball. The bat is like a club with one side flattened and must not be more than four and a quarter inches wide and thirty-eight inches in length. The ball is about the size of an orange, weighs between five and a half and five and three-quarter ounces and is bound in red leather. The captains of the teams toss a coin to decide who shall bat first. To start the match, two members of the batting side stand with their bats, one before each wicket. The other team becomes the fielding side and nine of them are scattered around the cricket field. The remaining two are the bowler and the wicketkeeper and they place themselves one behind each wicket. The bowler's duty is to hurl the ball from his wicket to the other. If he knocks down the stumps, the batsman is out. The batsman uses his bat to defend his wicket from the ball. In so doing he will deflect the ball about the cricketfield and the nine fieldsmen then try to retrieve it. The batsmen can attempt to run between the wickets thereby scoring runs. . . ."

Thirty-five minutes, with Spiros helping out, I kept them standing there, unable to get an alpha in edgeways, while I took them through the rules of our native ritual, the umpires' duties, field-placing, elementary tactics, and general etiquette on and off the field of play. Agro whispered feverishly at the back, but before he could mount a counterattack an old lady piped up with a question.

"Crick-et, wick-et," she clucked. "This one man has the square leg? How so?"

I gave them a further fifteen minutes on the vocabulary of fielding and they were so taken by the mystery of the Third Man and the elegance of Fine Leg that they departed without further mention of the alien olive pressers. Their gentle, marvelling murmur of "crick-et, wick-et . . . wick-et, crick-et" faded down the street like an outing of cicadas.

Next came fourteen members of the Federation of Painters and Decorators. Their spokesman carried a whitewash brush as his wand of office and asked that military transport be used to lift limestone from a deserted Government dump. Crudely, without any finesse, I just gave him the feed line right away.

"I'm sorry. I couldn't do that. It just wouldn't be cricket."

"Crick-et?" he said, scrubbing his beard with the brush. "What, please, is crick-et?"

"Crick-et," I rattled off like a Stratford guide, "is a game played between two teams of eleven players. It is played on a cricket pitch which is twenty-two yards in length and has three stumps, twenty-eight inches high and set nine inches wide, at either end. Each set of stumps . . ."

I had my facts straight at this second reading and rolled monotonously over them for fully forty-five minutes while they stood before me opening and closing their mouths like handicapped goldfish. Sergeant Transom's spirits had risen enormously by now and he took over and gave a good twenty minutes on the scorer's duties and the science of bowling analysis. By the time Agro and Spiliou got them outside, there were three delegations piled up on the stairs, an hour behind schedule and greeking rebelliously.

The Transport and General Workers Union came next, complaining that Army drivers were taking their business on the side.

"Such action would be quite unfair," I said. "It would simply not be cricket."

The two marshals shushed fiercely and nobody asked what was crick-et.

"If our drivers did that," I went on, "they would definitely not be playing the game."

"What game?" asked a puzzled mechanic.

"Cricket," I rapped back. "Which is a game played between two teams of eleven players. It is played on a cricket pitch which is twenty-two yards in length and has three stumps, twenty-eight inches high and set nine inches wide, at either end . . ."

I gave them the full recital, an hour and a quarter of purest Wisden, and when I got to the difference between no, dead, and lost balls, the conveners lugged them out by main force.

The day was done by that time and the other deputations had to wait till next morning. They were well drilled overnight and when the Dolia Working Men's Glee Club filed in, every man was tight-lipped and wary. I tried them with cricket and play the game, but none would take the bait.

"If the British soldiers can get drunk and sing on Saturday nights, why," asked the bass-profundo, "cannot Greek peoples march in the Square and sing the 'Red Flag' on Sunday nights?"

"That," said Sergeant Transom, "is a very crafty question. In fact, a regular googly."

"Goog-lee? What, please, is goog-lee?"

"A tricky ball in cricket. And cricket is a game played between two teams of eleven players. It is played on a cricket pitch . . ."

He took them right through the usual routine and I did a bit of a Cardus on "A Few Cricketing Characters" before we let them go.

[215]

I caught the next lot inside a minute by saying their argument had me dead leg-before.

"Leg before what, please?"

"Wicket. As in cricket which is a game played between two teams of eleven players . . ."

The two commissars came wearily on with fresh deputations but, whichever way they played it, we got round to cricket in the end. If the petitioners resisted my known gambits we lured their curiosity on to the field with new ones—yorkers, body-line or tail-ender.

Just before tea on this second afternoon of my flannelled filibuster, Agro and Spiliou conceded the match. They'd heard our monologue eleven times and just couldn't take any more. The fact that I'd been doing it in my John Arlott impersonation for the last three recitals may have been the final stroke that broke them down. The word had gone round, too, that all you got in my office was an iliad of cricket, and they couldn't get people to join their deputations any more.

We were teaching Spiros to play cribbage that evening of victory when the Swede and Madame burst in together.

"Dis is de night," boomed the Swede, "I have seen dem massing in de mountains. Thousands and thousands of dem with big guns and small guns and sharpening knives. It is tonight for sure dey come to cut everybody's throats."

"He's right, Captain," cried Madame. "That Iliou plays my piano, he see his brother Tasos today and he tell him stay off the streets tonight because ELAS coming to kill the English."

Spiros looked up from taking one for his nob.

"Not to worry, nobody," he said. "Let the ELAS come. We will talk to them. They will be glad to go back to the mountains. Sir Lieutenant Goodbody will tell them about cricket."

"Crick-et?" said the Swede. "What is crick-et?"

[216]

"Cricket," said Spiros, "is an English game played between two teams of eleven players. It is played on a pitch . . ."

Whether Iliou told the ELAS about the cricket lecture that might be awaiting them, I never found out. Anyway, they didn't come that night and within a week we were ordered to proceed hotfoot back to Athens. As we pulled out of Dolia, they were setting up wickets made from olive branches in the Square. The Working Men's Glee Club were in the field, the umpires were Agro and Spiliou, and the opening batsmen of the Combined Trade Unions XI were taking guard with herculean clubs flattened on one side but clearly measuring not more than four and a quarter inches in width and thirty-eight inches in length.

Which just went to prove, as I pointed out to Sergeant Transom, that the British Army is always right in the end. Our refresher course in Recreational Training—Cricket on the purgatory of F27 had not been, after all, just another moonstruck, military waste of time.

Chapter Seventeen

The winning of the battle and the losing of it, are exercises of the human intelligence and the human will. . . . The general who made the plan for a successful battle will believe that his plan was the prime cause of success; but the company commander and his company who have fought all day . . . will remain convinced that it was they who tipped the balance towards victory. . . . The evidence of both may be as true as the human mind can make it, and yet fall short of perfect truth. . . .

ERIC LINKLATER
The Campaign in Italy

PEACE AND UNEMPLOYMENT was never the lot of the Musketeers and we were geeted in Athens with the news that the Division was off to France. We embarked at Piraeus and endured once again the ritual tortures laid down in Troop Transport Regulations.

We marched, laden like kleptomaniac refugees, to the appointed dock which, of course, was utterly shipless. After standing for the customary hour in drizzling rain we were told to move three-quarters of a mile across to the other side of the harbour. There we were shepherded on to a ship and urged to thread our ponderous way below. But being old sea-transport campaigners and familiar with the conventions, we waited patiently on deck for the next, inevitable move. It came, obedient to tradition, after twenty-five minutes . . . we were on the wrong ship. We were on the *Otranto*. We should be on the *Orontes* which was now waiting at a dock two hundred yards from where we had started.

[218]

Humping up once again, pack and kitbag, blanket and rifle, we were herded like cattle back across the harbour. We mounted the gangways of the *Orontes,* urged on by Embarkation Officers in brand new Service dress. The company moved in single file, following coloured arrows directing us to Mess Deck D14, down companionways, up ladders, and through a winding maze of metal corridors designed for the passage of emaciated midgets. The arrows, in conformity with T.T. Regulations, led us on a general tour of the ship's intestines, taking in such places of interest as the galley, sick bay and engine rooms. We never, of course, went anywhere near Mess Deck D14 but came back, in the natural order of things, to the exact point on the deck from which we had started.

Since we were experienced in embarkation protocol this caused us no perturbation and we set off once again into the underworld, turning at each junction in the opposite direction to that recommended by the arrows. Our conga of armed coolies clattered like a weary, hobnailed snake in and out of the red lead tunnels until in due course the head arrived at the entrance to Mess Deck D14. The mess deck, in accordance with Cocker, was already packed full of troops. They were, as usual, the Black Watch. Never, throughout the duration of the war, did the Musketeers arrive at their allotted mess deck but to find every hammock, table and bench jam-packed with glowering, beetle-browed Scots.

It was at this point in any embarkation that the Musketeers would start baaing. The bawl would break up first from those in sight of the occupied mess deck and those behind would pass back the message that once again we were homeless on shipboard.

"Baa . . . baa . . . bay . . . baa . . . baa . . . bay . . . baa!

In tenor, bass, alto, and falsetto the plaintive bleating would be taken up along the endless chain of cheated men, queueing, stooped in small steel culverts, miserable, helpless, and loaded like martial Christmas trees.

"Baa . . . baa . . . bay . . . baa . . . baa!"

It was the soldier's ultimate censure upon those whose bungling had brought him to this pass. . . . If we are to be treated like sheep, then we will protest like sheep. . . . The stupid sound expressed a scorn beyond the power of words and, once provoked, spread throughout every sinew of the ship, echoed by those standing in other bowels in similar plight and by the rest, more fortunate, who were already ensconced in Calcutta black-hole comfort.

"Baa . . . bay . . . baa . . . baa . . . bay!"

All through the dreary process of turning everybody about and threading the needle back the way we had come, the contemptuous bleating went on and its wordless condemnation drove the ship's officialdom raving mad.

"Stop your men making that damned noise," snorted the purple-faced colonel who was resident O.C. Ship. "Order them to stop that baaing at once."

"Ordering them won't stop it, I'm afraid," said Major Arkdust. "There's only one way to make them stop."

"And what the hell's that?"

"Show them an empty mess deck. That always works."

And so they wound us yet again, in and out and round about and finally into an empty mess deck. The mighty cargo of sheep vanished, the Musketeers baaed no more.

We duly performed the human chain rituals whereby rifles and kitbags were passed from hand to hand of a hundred men down into parts adjacent to the bilge water, there to lie inert till the morrow when it would be discovered that they were in the wrong holds and a really intricate game of pass-the-parcel could be organized to change them over. By the time this had been finally achieved we would be approaching our destination, of course, and the whole lot, the labels conveniently torn off the rifles, would have to be sent up along the human conveyor belt all over again.

My cup of weariness flowed over on my chin when we finally went afloat and Captain Tablet appointed me Ship's Duty Officer for the ensuing twenty-four hours. My list of duties included the task of ensuring that all decks were cleared of Army personnel by midnight and that all khaki-coloureds were by then battened down below. Fortunately the soldiers, done brown by naval cooperation, were only too happy to hit their hammocks. But, although my midnight chore was easy, it did provide me with one of the most disturbing experiences of my Army career.

I found only one night bird, stretched out in a reclining chair on the officer's sun deck. He was draped in a strange, pale leather jerkin and his rank was hidden from view. A glass hung in his hand, a dying bottle of gin and a jug of water sat beside him.

"Duty Officer," I said. "Time to go below."

"Sit down, Duty Officer," he said, waving the glass majestically and spilling alcohol on my boots. "Just you and me and the man in the moon. Have a drink."

I hesitated, doubtful what to do. He spoke with an air of authority. I couldn't see his rank. He could see mine and clearly wasn't unduly scared even though I was a full lieutenant. He seemed in his early thirties, lean and wiry, his thick hair gone early grey.

"Sit down, Duty Officer," he said. "Nobody'll know. I'll write you a chit for the King. Have a drink."

I sat down.

"Musketeer, eh?" he said. "One of the willing horses. Exploited by tradition. It's time they gave you poor buggers a rest."

"The Musketeers," I said, "serve wherever their King and Country need them."

"That's what I said. Exploited by tradition. You learnt that mouthful parrot-fashion at the depot. They indoctrinate you with guff like Jesuits with Sunday school kids. That's how they make fighting soldiers. That's how they keep you going chest-high to the guns. Worst thing you can do in time of war, old chap, is to join a famous fighting formation."

"I am proud," I said coldly, "to be a Musketeer."

"Maybe, but you're a mug as well. Think it out. Africa, Italy, Greece, and now France. They flog the good fighting units. They exploit the military mugs. If you'd got yourself in some nice, inefficient, nondescript outfit you'd be sitting on your thick end now guarding the pacifists of Cairo or the pipelines of Persia. Instead of going off to storm the Rhine. They treat you up-Guards-and-at-'em boys like pale-faced Gurkhas. . . . See that hill with the guns on top! Run up it, there's good chaps, till you drop down dead. . . . Japan . . . that's where they'll have you next. Soon as Europe's over it'll be all the willing horses hotfoot for Japan. . . . Have a drink to all the willing little horses . . ."

He charged his glass and held it out.

"No, thank you. I do not drink on duty."

"Oh-ho! A serious Musketeer." He drank it himself. "Never take war too seriously. That's the trouble with the Aryans. They still take war seriously. The only nation that really knows anything about war is the Italians. They were engaged in scientific warfare when we were painting our arses bright blue and the Teutons were still copulating with apes. The Italians have had war. They've grown out of it. They've seen through it. They're the only true realists who know what to do about war. . . . As soon as you're in it, get out of it. . . . Get back to the important things of life like vino and Verdi and vulnerable virgins. Leave the knockdown, drag out stuff to those not yet civilized enough to despise it . . ."

"But if we did that," I said, "we'd just get beaten by the Germans and that . . ."

"We should have been beaten by the Germans already," he broke in, "if we hadn't been so dead lucky as to have Hitler on their side. It's only the way little old Adolf keeps on interfering with his generals that saves us from paying for the botchery of our own. . . . What's the biggest battle going on in France right now?"

"Er . . . the Battle of the Reichswald?"

"Wrong. . . . The battle between Montgomery and Bradley. For the history book title of "The Man Who Won the War." If they spent as much time out-scheming the Boche as they do at circumventing each other, we'd all be in Berlin by now. Poor old Eisenhower can barely get a clear weekend on the golf course without being called off the fifteenth to separate them. They were steamed up fit for personal fisticuffs during the Battle of the Bulge. If von Runstedt had been smart enough to withdraw sharply from between them, they'd have smacked together and had it out there and then, boot and bare knuckle in the Ardennes. . . . Generals! . . . Phwtt! . . ." He spat metaphorically. "Prestige-chasers! . . . Megalomania-mongers! . . . Thank God for Hitler!"

The Duty Officer's Orders gave no guidance as to the action to be taken against defeatist talk on the high seas, but I felt obliged to speak up for our gallant generals.

"You exaggerate," I said. "Our generals are fine, responsible men. Someone has to have the courage to make tremendous decisions. Someone has to make mistakes . . ."

"Too true, boy," he broke in, "but there's no call to make a way of life out of mismanagement. Did you see them bomb the abbey at Cassino?"

"Yes."

"Just an example. Fourth Indian were up there on Snakeshead Ridge ordered to attack straight after the bombardment was done. They fixed the date. They fixed the time. They told the Fourth Indian . . . then they decided to bomb a day earlier. They dropped leaflets on the monastery telling the monks when they were going to bomb it . . . They told the Italians, they told the Germans, they told the generals . . . they told everybody except Fourth Indian up there on the ridge. And the first they knew about the time going forward a day was when bombs landed on them instead of Cassino. Even Hitler couldn't save them from that."

He poured himself some more gin at the memory and took a restoring swig.

"But they were lucky the Air Force was operating normally and kept its usual quota of bombs outside the immediate target area. God knows if they hit any Germans in Cassino, but they knocked hell out of Venafro, fifteen miles away, and wrote off a hundred and forty civilians. They straddled Eighth Army Headquarters which wasn't a bad thing to do, bashed our own gun lines and killed forty-four artillerymen, and blew up a Moroccan hospital to knock off forty patients. . . . When they have a count-up after this war I reckon they'll find the Allied Air Forces dropped more bloody bombs on us than they did on the enemy."

"Really," I said, "you are quite unfair . . ."

"Am I indeed?" He wobbled upright in offence and poured more gin over my boots. "Souk-el-Arba. What about that? . . . Miles behind the lines, and blasted to hell by bombers sent to hit Kasserine. Hundred miles off target that time, and Eisenhower paid fifty thousand quid compensation. . . . And remember those yellow identification triangles? You had them, didn't you? In North Africa, tied under your chin like a bib. When approached by Allied aircraft, they said, hold the points of the triangle at arms length to establish your identity. And what happened if you ever did that thing?" He fixed me with an accusing finger. "What happened when you stood out like a nit with your little yellow flag? Answer me that, matey."

"They machine-gunned us," I said. "But that was just an isolated mistake . . ."

"So was I. God knows how many poor trusting bastards met their Maker standing in the middle of the road extending those yellow triangles. They were good for only one thing. Making tops for nurses' bikinis. And then the dye used to run in salt water and turn their busts bright yellow. Indelible it was too and never came off. I know because my brother, Conrad, married a North African, yellow-breasted, nursing sister twelve months ago and he can still wake up wondering if he's in the top half of a Chinese brothel. . . . Do you know my brother, Conrad?"

[224]

"No," I said. "Hadn't you better get below now, it's gone half past twelve."

"Must tell you about my brother, Conrad. Another little drink, another little talk . . ." He was rambling drunk by now but his tongue never seemed to falter. "My brother, Conrad, won the Battle of Alamein. Now you tell me, Mr. Musketeer, what was Alamein?"

"It was," I said patiently, "a famous victory."

"It was," he levelled the gin bottle like a cannon, "one bloody great mistake."

"Nonsense. We won it magnificently."

"One bloody great mistake. From beginning to end. But the benevolent God Mighty in Battle, the Christian monopoly of British brass hattery, reached down the hand he uses on wandering babies and drunken sailors and saw us safely through. Him and my brother, Conrad. . . . Very clever chap is Conrad. Very important staff chap back down in Cairo. Never came out of Cairo on account of his maps. Had a warehouse big as Buckingham Palace full of maps. He had hundreds and thousands of maps all over Africa. Whatever happened on the Dark Continent, it could never take my brother, Conrad, by surprise. You want to fight a war anywhere in Africa, beat up the Boers in Bloemfontein or conquer the cannibals up the Congo, you only had to ask my brother, Conrad, and he'd let you have the maps in a jiffy. A wonderful filing system he had to keep all those maps straight, especially when the map numbers keep repeating themselves every hundred sheets. And with half the desert maps a blank sheet of nothing it was a tricky job making sure you picked them from the right hemisphere. Conrad was a marvel at map selection and he never made a mistake till Alamein. What with Montgomery abolishing the back-to-Palestine plan and calling up his getaway truck, Conrad's nerves were in a terrible state when Eighth Army Headquarters sent down their requisition. He went to pieces and met it from the wrong shelf. He sent them up sheets with the right

[225]

numbers on but from the wrong set, a hundred or so sheets to the south. He found out his mistake mind you, a fortnight later when he was taking stock, but by then the battle was joined and there was nothing anyone could do about it."

"You're not trying to tell me," I said, "that Montgomery fought the Battle of Alamein off the wrong maps."

He drew up his shoulders in tipsy dignity.

"My brother, Conrad, sent them to him. There was bugger-all on half of them, but flat sand and one contour. Just the Kidney Feature to break the forty-mile monotony and a bit of a dip down by the Qattara Depression. So they marked up their start lines and their axes and their bounds and fought their chinagraph battle quite happily on the sheets that Conrad gave them. While the troops were fighting on the sands of El Alamein, Eighth Army Headquarters were conducting their paper battle a thousand miles to the south on a bare bit of lower Libyan desert two hundred miles northwest of Khartoum."

"But yet," I said swiftly, "we still won the battle."

"My brother, Conrad, won the battle. If he'd sent them up the right maps to work off they'd probably have lost it. Got to finding out where the troops really were and interfering with them. They appreciated it too, you know, because they gave my brother, Conrad, a medal. They gave him the M.B.E. for meritorious issue of maps in Cairo. And you don't get medals for nowt, do you?"

"No," I said, "of course you don't."

"You get medals, old cock, for pulling the general's chest-nuts out of the fire. Medals are isued *pro rata* to the magni-tude of the blunder made by the higher command. You can't fight against impossible odds unless some bloody brass hat is incompetent enough to land you up against impossible odds. You can't conduct an heroic last-man, last-round defence un-less some red-tabbed genius has bungled his battle and left you on your tod. . . . The bigger the boob, the more the medals. The number of gongs given after an action increases in direct proportion to the number of casualties. In lauding the decorated living, we overlook the wasted dead. Our attention focused on the gallantry of the survivors we forget the top-level botchery that caused the casualties. . . . Ten thousand killed today, sir! Strike up the band! Lob out the V.C.'s! And make me a Field Marshal!"

He tipped up the bottle and poured the last of the gin into his glass.

"Medals . . ." he said, lurching in his chair. "Do you know the one thing you got to have to get medals?"

"Courage?"

"Wrong again. You're wrong every time, Mr. Musketeer. There's plenty of courage about. Plenty of blokes too stupid to take cover. Plenty of blokes got no imagination, too dull to know the danger, too dumb to run away. Plenty of blokes, half-crazy, half-animal, best they can think to do is to lower the horns and charge. . . . Just being brave don't get no medals. There's a thousand heroes every day but no laurels go to the unsung . . . you get no garlands if nobody hears what you've done. And the biggest medals don't go to the biggest heroes . . . they go to the ones with the best reports. . . . It's the reports, cocky, that win the medals, the citations that capture the gongs. . . . Brave man—good citation—big medal!"

He banged his chest like Tarzan and knocked himself off the chair. "Bravest man in the world—poor citation—no medal! That's the way of it, boy. If you want to get medals, you want a literate C.O. And a lousy general to make the boobs. . . . You want a colonel like I had, boy, lead writer for a national daily, every word a masterpiece, every syllable hitting them in the heart. . . . The Hemingway of the war diary, the Dostoeyevsky of the dispatch . . ."

I got my hands under his shoulders and lugged him to his feet.

"Come on," I said. "It's nearly one o'clock. You'd better get to bed."

"Where's my bottle?" he grumbled. "Who stole my bottle?"

He lit a cigarette lighter and swung it like a torch.

"Ah! There it is."

"Put that light out," I said. "There might be ships watching us."

"What ships?"

"Enemy ships."

He held the bottle to his eye like a telescope.

"I see no ships," he said. "Stand the sea at ease." He swung back his jerkin as he turned wobbling towards the companionway. It was then that I saw he had a V.C., two D.S.O.'s and three rows of variegated ribbon.

It really was a most disturbing experience, and I would have made a special security report to O.C. Ship had I not been fully extended for the rest of the voyage in that interminable naval game of lugging the rifles and kitbags out of whichever hold they happened to be in and dropping them momentarily in another.

Chapter Eighteen

By now enemy resistance west of the Rhine had fallen into confusion.
. . . From Dusseldorf to Coblenz a score of heavy bridges collapsed
into the Rhine as crews touched off their demolitions. Although eager
to secure a Rhine river bridgehead we had despaired of taking a bridge
intact. . . . Suddenly my phone rang. It was Hodges calling from Spa.
"Brad," Courtney called . . . "Brad, we've gotten a bridge."
"A bridge? You mean you've gotten one intact on the Rhine?"
"Yep . . ."
"Hot dog, Courtney," I said, "this will bust him wide open. . . ."
GEN. OMAR BRADLEY
A Soldier's Story

WHEN TWELVE PLATOON joined the Allied Forces in Western
Europe the forward troops were closing up on the Rhine. I
was most gratified to find that we were in time to take part in
the greatest opposed river-crossing of the War because, in
spite of all the rivers we met in Italy, we were never lucky
enough to cross any of them before the enemy had pulled
out. An opposed river crossing is one of the most interesting
maneuvers a military commander can be called upon to un-
dertake and I was sorry, in so river-racked a land as Italy, not
to have sampled its complexities.

Progress from Rimini to Bologna had been something of
an aquatic Grand National. Water jumps appeared at regular
intervals—Conca, Marrechia, Savio, Ronco, Montone, and the
rest—and only the tooth-stumps of blown bridges remained to
help us over. It wasn't due to lack of trying that Twelve

Platoon never crossed a river till someone had built a bridge. It was just an infernal sequence of bad luck.

We were all set for watermanship on the Marrechia and they sent us up six inflatable rubber boats. It was depressing to find on pumping them up that each had suffered a two-inch slit *en route*.

"Must have been a chisel or something sticking out in the truck the engineers brought them in," said Corporal Dooley. "Terrible careless with their tools they are. We'll not be getting over in these, sir. A great disappointment it is, too, with the men all raring to go."

"Don't give up," I said. "We can still make the assault. Get the puncture outfit from the fifteen-hundredweight and we'll mend the holes."

It took most of the night to get the little patches built up along the slits. When we finally had the boats airtight again, Corporal Hink, overly eager for the fray, treadled the pump with such astonishing vigour that it shot out from under his boot like a football and disappeared into the muddy torrent of the Marrechia. By fixing a piece of gas tubing over the valve and lining up the platoon for relay balloon blowing, I managed to rouse the flaccid black rubber to the wrinkled inflation of a Zulu grandmother's bosom. But though the chaps gallantly puffed themselves blue-faced and thyroid-eye-balled, we never got a boat to a state of buoyancy. And by the time Major Arkdust had sent us up a new pump the Boche had withdrawn and the engineers could build in peace.

When we were faced by the flooded reaches of the Ronco they sent us up canvas assault boats which collapsed flat for transport and opened up on an ingenious wooden frame-work. We taped the launching routes over the mud flats, rehearsed the landing, and hid the boats in the bushes. At Z minus 15 we erected the craft—to find that they collapsed immediately under our hands. The main struts at bow and stern were cut completely through and there was no way of changing the spineless bag of canvas into a navigable craft.

"It looks like sabotage," I said. "These are saw marks. Perhaps a German swam across during the night."

Sergeant Transom looked expertly at the severed pieces of wood.

"These ain't saw marks, sir. They've been gnawed through. It'll be the water rats that done it."

"But do water rats eat wood?"

"Round here they do, sir. All the time. The giant Italian wood-eating water rat. That's what done in those assault boats, sir, and a real danger to other river crossing parties they might well be. We were lucky ours were hungry ones and chewed right through. If they'd had full stomachs and stopped halfway through, the frame could have collapsed out there in the middle and drowned the lot of us."

I deemed it in the best general interest to write a report for Major Arkdust there and then on the dangers of the giant Italian wood-eating water rat, accompanied by sketches of a suggested metal assault boat framework which would be resistant to rodent teeth. By the time I had finished and the pioneer corporal had come up to repair the struts, the Germans had once again gone away and we were able to cross the Ronco in daylight and dry-shod.

Our advance halted by the Montone, they sent forward wagon loads of kapok-bridging—buoyant lozenges about five feet by two which could be laid like floatable railway sleepers to support a duckboard track. Sappers stood waist-deep all one night knitting a floating bridge of the right length. It lay anchored by day among the reed forest against our bank. We set off to tow it across the following night and as it snaked clear of the bullrushes and into the current it broke at every joint and the individual portions of kapok went zipping down the river like big, black dominoes.

"All the lashings have broken away," I said.

"It's them blasted Italian water rats again," said Sergeant Transom.

"But I thought they ate wood?"

[231]

"That was down on the Ronco. Up here on the Montone they eat rope as well."

The sapper sergeant got very excited as his bridge disappeared piecemeal downstream and threatened to sue somebody about it. He dived in and collected up pieces of rat-cut rope and was waving them excitedly in my face when Corporal Globe unfortunately slipped on the mudbank and hit him across the back of the head with the thick end of his antitank rifle. We had to send him back unconscious to the F.D.S., and I took the opportunity to send with the driver to Major Arkdust an addendum to my earlier Water Rat Report explaining the rope appetite of the Montone mutation.

Brought up short by the Lamone they pushed up to us an ingenious engineer with a rocket, cable, and pulley wheels. It was the plan to shoot over a line in shipwreck fashion and, if no enemy ill feeling arose, to dispatch a swimming patrol to secure it. Our end would then be fixed to a higher purchase and we would each in turn roll gently across in a breeches buoy.

"When," asked Corporal Hink, after I had explained the technique to my order group, "are they sending up the roundabouts and coconut shies? Where do they reckon we are? Butlin's flipping Holiday Camp?"

That afternoon the rocketeer mounted his giant firework on its special tripods and made abstruse calculations to set the elevation and line of fire. It was unfortunate that all my N.C.O.'s were still non-swimmers and I had, therefore, to lead the swimming patrol myself. Sergeant Transom was giving me a final coating of used engine oil, just before midnight, when the engineer went through the countdown and fired his rocket. It fizzed quietly on the trestle for a few moments . . . gave a sudden whoosh of smoke . . . grew to a driving roar as one leg of the front tripod pulled away . . . the whole device fell sideways and the rocket blasted off at right angles to the river . . . turned back over our heads for two

[232]

hundred yards, hit the front window of the Company Headquarters farmhouse . . . crashed straight through and out the
back, threading the needle with the cable as it went.

It happened, unfortunately, that Major Arkdust was sleeping directly under the path of the cable and, as it streaked
like an aerial snake across his ceiling he got the idea that
Twelve Platoon was deliberately attempting his assassination
by rocket fire. This misconception was reinforced as the
whizzbang came finally to rest and an Italian flag, which had
somehow got caught in the end of the cable, fell to the floor
and draped his camp bed like a catafalque. He appeared rapidly at my launching site and although I did my best to explain to him the true course of events, it was difficult to do
justice to Twelve Platoon's defence standing to attention on
a mud flat, stark naked, and plastered from head to foot with
used engine oil.

After such a series of riverside misfortunes, the prospect of
the assault on the Rhine filled me with elation. The Division
had landed at Marseilles and *en route* northwards to join 21st
Army Group stayed at the beginning of March with American First Army. Twelve Platoon was encamped on the banks
of the Echler, a tributary of the Rhine, twenty miles up from
its junction with the great river. We were allocated four
American rubber boats for river-crossing exercises. Compared
with the overgrown inner tubes we had in Italy, they were
inflatable palaces. They blew themselves up from gas bottles,
had built-in spray sheets and were covered in little pockets
containing chocolate, chewing gum, signal flares, bandages,
and best wishes to our brave boys over there from the man-
agement and staff of the Rochford (N.Y.) Rubber Goods
Company.

"Get a band up front there playing Water Music," said
Corporal Globe, "and a couple of Wogs with ostrich feather
fans, and Antony could take Cleopatra twice round the pier
in that gondola."

[233]

I devised an embarkation drill specially suited to our latex luxury liners and spent a day practising it on a sandbank. Knowing that battles are won in the hearts of the soldiers I took my usual steps to ensure that everyone under my command was firmly in the picture.

"We will shortly be embarking, men," I said, after breaking ranks to relax the tension, "on the decisive battle of the whole war—the Assault on the Rhine. The Musketeers will, as ever, be in the forefront of the battle. I am determined, as I know you all are, to obtain pride of place in the assault for Twelve Platoon. It is my intention when the Musketeers attack the Rhine that Twelve Platoon shall be their spearhead. But we will not win this place of honour merely because I happen to be the senior platoon commander in the Regiment. We will win it only on merit . . . only if we can show Colonel Plaster that we are the outstanding exponents of watermanship under his command. And we can achieve that reputation only by hard work and intensive training. From now until we are called to battle, I propose to practice watermanship each day and to hold an embarkation and landing exercise on the Echler each night. Then, when the trumpets sound the last Great Call to Arms, Twelve Platoon will be first into the water, first across the Rhine and first on the road to Berlin!"

"And last," said Private Drogue, jocularly concealing his enthusiasm, "on the bleeding leave roster."

"How wide, sir," asked Corporal Dooley, "did you say the Rhine is likely to be?"

"Rather more than a quarter of a mile wide."

"Khee-rist!" said Private Spool.

"Then it'll be slow running?" asked Corporal Hink.

"I'm afraid not. The river is heavily swollen by the winter rains." I never believed in softening the facts to my men. "There will be a strong current and we will need all the watermanship at our command."

"Blimey!" said Private Clapper.

"And which bank is the higher," asked Corporal Globe, "theirs or ours?"

"Theirs. They hold the commanding slopes and we must pay particular attention in our training to the use of cover after landing."

"Cut my throat!" said Private Gripweed.

"What will the going be like?" asked Sergeant Transom. "Better than Italy?"

"No. It may well be worse. Much of the east bank is precipitous. At the likely crossing places there may well be mud flats to negotiate."

"Quarter of a mile across," said Private Drogue. "Jerry up on top, pouring of bleeding rain, and up to your crutch in mud. . . . Rah, rah, rah! chaps. Tally-ho! and good hunting!"

"That's the spirit," I said. "Obstacles are made to be overcome. Where there's a will there's a way. Now we'll just go through the details of tonight's exercise . . ."

At midnight we were down on the sandbank with our boats. The sections crouched back under cover of the bracken as Sergeant Transom and I crawled forward with the guide tapes. The river swung in a curve before us, swollen with winter rain, racing fast with white water breaking against the far bank.

"Right!" I commanded quietly. "Inflating parties forward."

Out of the darkness came the boat-carriers and unrolled their parcels along the tapes. Compressed air hissed softly and the rubber creaked as the craft grew like monster slugs and slipped silently into the water.

"Secure boats!"

A stake was driven into the sand and the painters from all four boats were tied to it. The ropes stretched out taut and straining as the current pulled greedily at the airy craft.

"Prepare to embark!"

[235]

The sections came crawling forward from the undergrowth and crouched in correct boat-mounting order on the cross-tape before the stake, N.C.O.'s in front, paddle men at their stations.

"Embark! Follow me!"

I ran forward through the shallows, leapt into my command craft and took my place at the prow. As I turned to watch my troops embarking the boat suddenly shot out into mid-stream. . . . The line had come away from the stake before anyone could join me . . . I was alone on board and gaining speed every second as the current sucked me away into fast water. . . .

"Halt!" I cried. "Exercise Seaboots temporarily suspended. . . ."

I sensed the shadow of an overhanging tree coming up behind me . . . my feathery skiff swirled into a rapid, leapt for a moment bodily out of the water. . . . Leaves and twigs brushed past my face . . . my feet tangled, I lost my balance . . . a branch thumped me blindingly on the back of the head and I fell face down and out cold in the indiarubber scuppers.

When I came round the first flicker of dawn was touching the darkness. The water slapped and gurgled under my ear, and as I pulled myself up I felt a lump like a bony goitre on the overhang of my skull. My craft was skimming along on a vast expanse of roaring water. I could see no banks on either side and thought at first that I had been swept out to sea. Huge tangled shapes appeared above me in the sky, and I realized I was passing under the skeleton of a blown bridge. The light grew steadily stronger and I picked up the shape of cliffs away in the distance both to the port and starboard . . . I was on the Rhine and my pneumatic cockleshell was speeding on the flood at a whipping ten knots.

I looked at my watch. It was 04.30 hours. I had been going for about four hours. Allowing for the twenty miles of the

[236]

Echler, I would have been racing for about two hours down the Rhine.

There were no paddles in the boat—in my special drill they were issued against signature to the crew members. I searched the craft, but although I unearthed plenty of chewing gum, field-dressings, candy, and a sexy letter from Myra Kegover of the Rochford Rubber Goods Company inviting the finder to call her up for a good time when on leave, I found nothing to paddle with. I was helpless in the swift current, unable to divert the boat to the home bank or to prevent it grounding on the enemy side. Buildings sprung up on the German flank, and with daylight now up I deemed it wise to lie flat in the bottom of the boat again and make an appreciation of my situation.

There were three courses open to me. One, if the boat came up on the east bank I would have to find a hiding place and lie low till the Allies advanced. Two, if it finished on the west bank, I could make my way by night to the American lines. Three, if, as seemed likely from the pace I was going, the Rhine kept me driving straight down the middle and out to sea, I would have to pin my faith in the Royal Navy. As long as I lay flat in the bottom of the craft, the Boche would think it a piece of untenanted flotsam and I calculated that there was sufficient chewing gum and candy aboard to keep me alive for a week.

I was working out my likely time of arrival in the North Sea when the dinghy found a fourth alternative. It stopped in the middle of the river. I could feel obstructions pushing at both rubber sides and I peeked gingerly over the gunwales. To my right rose the concrete pier of a bridge, on my left lay the weed-tangled mass of a tree swept down the river and trapped against the stonework. Up above, the bridge towered from bank to bank, intact and unblown. I was completely hidden from view between the branches of the tree and the face of the pier. I clambered out on to the trunk and pulled

[237]

up the painter to make the boat secure. It was only half as long as it had been the night before. The end was frayed and tasselled, just like the ropes gnawed by the water rats of the Montone. I made a mental note to report that there was evidence of the same species on the Echler and a faster biting breed at that.

There was a maintenance ladder built into the western side of the pier leading up to the span. The tree screened it for much of the way and then it disappeared inside the curving line of the girderwork. If I got up there I could work my way along the underside of the bridge to the west bank. Carefully I climbed up the metal rungs . . . higher and higher above the rushing water . . . and had just reached the safety of the under-girders when there was a clink of metal behind and above me.

"Hände hoch! Kommen Sie hier."

A German soldier had me covered from a bay built out from the side of the bridge. If he fired from his twelve-feet range I was a goner. If I put my hands up then and there I would fall sixty feet on to the pier, the tree, or into the Rhine. There was no way out. I scrambled up the last few rungs on to the bridgeway and raised my hands above my head. Fortunately I had anticipated the possibility of capture and had already planned a line of escape.

"Nicht schiessen," I said. *"Ich bin Skorzeny-kommando."*

During the battle of the Ardennes, Otto Skorzeny, the Boche supercommando and rescuer of Mussolini, had infiltrated groups of Yankee-speaking Germans in American uniform behind the Allied lines. The odd one was still being picked up here and there, trying to get back to his own lines.

"Skorzeny?" exclaimed the sentry. *"Komm' mit."*

He kept me covered from behind, and I had no chance yet to bolt for it. We walked across the bridge and he motioned me into a reinforced signal hut at the end. An officer, a precise, middle-aged man with a tiny waxed Kaiser moustache,

[238]

was at a desk leafing through a magazine. The sentry fired off
a fusillade of German, gesticulating at me as Exhibit No. 1.
The captain put on a pair of slab-sided library glasses and
studied me carefully.

"*Skorzeny? Hein? Sitzen Sie.*"

I sat down. He dismissed the sentry and I heard the door
lock behind him. He opened a drawer of his desk and produced a mouth organ. Placing it to his lips, he fixed his eyes
on mine and burst suddenly forth into the commanding bars
of "God Save the King."

Automatically I rose from my chair and snapped to attention. As an officer holding His Majesty's Commission, I had
no alternative. The organist changed the tune abruptly to
"Colonel Bogey" than put down his instrument and chuckled
derisively.

"Just a little trick," he said, "I have invented to trap the
English. Sit down again, if you please. You are not one of
Skorzeny's men. You are a British engineer commando officer
sent in advance of your troops to prevent the demolition of
this bridge?"

I folded my arms defiantly. I was an experienced prisoner
by now, having been captured successively by the Arabs,
Poles, British, and Germans.

"I will tell you nothing but my name, rank, and number. I
am number 131313, Lieutenant Ernest Goodbody."

"They send you single-handed in your rubber boat by
night to sabotage the demolition wires. An officer sent on
such an important mission will be like Skorzeny, in direct
contact with the very highest level command. Perhaps even
briefed by Eisenhower himself . . . yes?"

"I am number 131313, Lieutenant Ernest Goodbody."

He leaned back in his chair, took off his glasses and rubbed
his eyes wearily.

"You are a brave officer. It was a most dangerous venture.
Your higher command must be desperate to obtain a bridge

[239]

over the Rhine . . ." He paused, leaned conspiratorially across the desk and emphasized his words with a finger wagging in my face. "To obtain a bridge across the Rhine . . . *undamaged and intact.*"

"I am number 131313, Lieutenant Ernest Goodbody."

As I drew back to save my nose from his fingernail, my eye was caught by a familiar cover on the magazine he had been reading. It was the *International Corn-Chandlers Trade Review and Quarterly Gazette.* There was a rubber stamp impression on the cover—"Gradheim and Koch, Silberplatz, Brunswick." My mind rushed immediately back to dear old Kettering and my office at Cawberry and Company. Many's the letter I had written to Gradheim and Koch, one of our main continental corn-chandling contacts.

"Good Lord!" I exclaimed. "Not you! At Gradheim and Koch's?"

He picked up the magazine and smiled ruefully. I thought for a moment he was going to kiss the rubber stamp.

"Yes," he said. "Heinrich Odlebog, Warehouse Manager, Gradheim and Koch, Brunswick."

"Ernest Goodbody," I said. "Chief Accountant, Cawberry and Company, Kettering, Northampton."

"Cawberry and Company!" He beamed so broadly that the tiny spikes of his moustache pricked into his cheeks. "Of Kettering! And you, so brave a man, like me, a corn-chandler."

For that moment, in the little signal hut, the war stopped. Corn-chandling, like love, knows no barriers. The language of lentils is international. Wars may come, wars may go, but the chicken food keeps cropping.

Odlebog stretched out a hand in the secret grip of the World Fraternity of Corn-Chandlers. I was about to reciprocate with the English knuckle twist when my patriotism flowed back. I nodded politely but refused his hand.

"No," he said, "perhaps you are right. . . . But to hear again of Cawberry and Company. So many happy memories

. . . taking me back to Brunswick . . . ah! to be back in the warehouse on Silberplatz."

He sniffed in fragrant memory of the clean, dry, corn-store smell. The points of his moustache dropped now in melancholy and he rubbed his eyes wearily once more. He was a very tired man. . . . An idea began to blossom at the back of my mind . . . my greatest victory might be yet to come . . . as a successful corn-chandler he would undoubtedly be a realist and therefore aware that Germany had already lost the war. And then there was his strange, repeated emphasis of the Allied need for an intact bridge. . . . Could I smell a deal? Left, someone said, can speak to Left; then corn-chandler can certainly speak to corn-chandler.

"As you say," I opened, "we want a bridge over the Rhine. We shall get one in the end even though we may have to build it ourselves. The small delay will make no difference. Germany has already lost the war. The longer you make us wait on the Rhine the deeper into Germany come the Russians from the East. Who do you wish to occupy your country, the Allies or the Russians?"

"*Gruss Gott!*" He shivered at the Soviet prospect. "The Russkies! Wild animals!"

"Then why destroy the bridges? Why destroy yourselves?" It was time to strike home. "Why not save your country from the Russians and make your own fortune? We need a bridge. You have this bridge. . . . How much do you want for it?"

All the weariness left him. This was what he had been angling for. He leaned across the table, alert and wary. This was business, not war.

"Twenty-five thousand pounds. To be deposited in Switzerland."

"Twenty-five thousand? That's ridiculous. Eisenhower would never pay it."

I would never be able to look Mr. Cawberry in the face again if I closed for the first offer from Gradheim and Koch.

"It's a fine bridge," said Odlebog. "Excellent strategic situation. Twenty-four thousand . . . as one corn-chandler to another."

"We would build one for less. Seventeen thousand. It's a bit farther south than we'd like."

"Seventeen thousand? And I am risking my life! They're shooting people already for not blowing bridges fast enough. Twenty-three thousand, take it or leave it."

"All right, then . . . in view of the personal danger, eighteen thousand. But not a penny more could we get past the accountants."

"Eighteen thousand? . . . Never! . . . You are joking? . . . Eighteen thousand may be a fair price for a road bridge. But this is a railway bridge. Very strong bridge. Take trains, tanks, anything. For such a bridge . . . I will be a fool . . . twenty-two thousand and five hundred."

"We'd sooner have a plain road bridge, actually. For a quick deal . . . my final offer . . . Nineteen thousand."

We went on bargaining for a cutthroat half an hour and I finally closed for twenty-one thousand two hundred and fifty pounds and a Safe Conduct to Switzerland. Not only had I upheld the reputation of Cawberry and Company, but I had also saved the Government three thousand seven hundred and fifty pounds. I don't suppose anyone else throughout the war made so direct a saving of public expenditure by just thirty minutes' work. Odlebog drew up a contract in duplicate which I signed for and on behalf of General D. Eisenhower, Supreme Commander, Allied Forces in Europe. He insisted on a sealing deposit and all I could muster without overdrawing my account was fifty pounds. I wrote him a personal cheque for that amount. It was laid down in the contract that when Odlebog was given the note of hand of an officer of general rank agreeing to his terms, he would hand over the plan of the demolition charges.

"I will tell the sentry who captured you that you are indeed a Skorzeny man and that now you are going back into the Allied territory. He will escort you down into the town and to the limit of our defences. After that, you will be on your own."

"I'll be back before dark," I said. "I'll make straight for the nearest American general."

"Good luck," he said. "And be careful. My future is in your hands."

The sentry led me for a mile beyond the town and left me on the outskirts of a wire-fringed forest. Following Odlebog's directions I made my way southwestwards through the scrub as fast as the ankle-deep peat would allow. After three-quarters of an hour I came to the edge of the pines and in view of a white road. As I worked my way down to it a convoy of German trucks came swirling back towards the bridge. I dived behind a clutter of rocks and was forced to lie there for a long time while odd parties of Boche infantry, dust-covered and downcast, struggled by in full retreat. It was gone three o'clock before the road was empty and I could safely move on. As I came out from behind the rocks there was a clatter of tracks around the bend ahead and a Sherman came grinding into view. I ran for the road waving my arms.

"Stop! Stop! I have a message for the general."

Three tanks swept by before I made the tarmac and three more ignored me as I tried to shout above the roar of their engines. Two armoured half-tracks loaded with American infantry rolled past me, but the third stopped as I stood steadfastly in its path waving my contract. A top sergeant leaned out.

"What the hell . . . Jesus! It's a Limey."

"Take me to your general," I said. "I have bought a bridge over the Rhine and must have his immediate approval."

"You bought a bridge?" His chewing gum fell from his dropped jaw. "How much you pay?"

"Fifty pounds down and twenty-one thousand two hun-

[243]

dred later. That's why I must see your general. I must have his promise to pay the rest."

He looked at me from head to foot, nodding rhythmically.

"Elmer!" he yelled suddenly. "Limey out front here says he just bought us a bridge. Fifty pounds down and four years to pay."

A prison-cropped, horn-rimmed face poked through my side of the canopy.

"Are you in charge?" I said.

"Yeah," he said like early Brando. "That's right. Me and Grover. We's in charge. You the guy bought a bridge?"

"Yes. I have the contract all signed up, right here. I insist that you take me immediately to your general."

"To the general? . . . Yeah, yeah . . . sure, sure. . . . You jump right in feller. Me and Grover take you to the general."

I climbed in the back. There was a wireless set grumbling away. The four soldiers made room for me.

"Poor bastard," said Elmer. "They must have brainwashed him or sump'n, Grover. Drove him straight round the bend."

"They put a bucket over their heads and belt it with pick handles till their brain pans is scrambled up all which-ways."

The truck drove on after the Shermans.

"Is this the way to your general?" I asked. "It is imperative he knows immediately that I have bought a bridge. Otherwise Odlebog might blow it up."

"Don't you worry nothing, bud," said Grover soothingly. "You're all right now. No Odlebug ain't going to get you. We gonna take you right straight to our general. Yes, sir! Right away . . ."

"When d'you escape?" asked Elmer. "They had you prisoner long?"

"No. Only about four hours. Please hurry . . ."

"Only four hours, Grover!" exclaimed Elmer. "Inhuman bastards. What they do to the poor guy to break him down mad-crazy in just four hours?"

"They got their methods," said Grover darkly. "Psychological, that's what they are. Bust up a feller's mind like that." He punched himself on the left temple. "Freud, Jung, Adler, all them head-shrinkers are goddamed Krauts."

"Look here," I said. "There's nothing wrong with me. I bought a bridge over the Rhine. I've got the contract to prove it. All I want . . ."

"All you want is twenty-one thousand two hundred quid and it's yours. We know. And we gonna see you get that money, ain't we, Elmer?"

"We sure are. So don't you worry none, bud. You just lie down and get some rest. You want for me to get you aspirin or sump'n, huh?"

"I don't want any aspirin, I told you . . ."

Suddenly the wireless sprang to blaring life.

"Elmer!" bawled the loudspeaker. "There's a bridge still standing. Get going hot-diggedy down there and start cutting wire!"

We topped the hill above the town and there below stood my bridge, intact and splendid.

"There it is," I said. "That's my property . . ."

The truck accelerated down the hill like a rocket, passing the two in front, and Elmer yelling instructions as he went by. Stirling Moss would have waved on those half-track drivers as they hammered round the bends, tore through the centre of town and out on to the riverside. . . . We were hitting sixty and in the shadow of the bridge when Elmer yelled "Halt!" and the driver slammed on all anchors . . . made a teeth-shattering Disney stop and pitched me out of my seat over the wireless and into the canvas gulf beyond.

Small arms fire rattled outside . . . the crump of the Shermans' guns and the hammering of their automatics beat down from the hill . . . an explosion rumbled up on the bridge, then another . . . men were running past the truck, yelling triumphantly. . . . I got my head out through the

[245]

front slit of the awning . . . the bridge stretched straight and unbroken into the heart of Germany . . . Odlebog was standing outside the signal hut waving his half of the contract . . . tommy guns crackled and he fell forward on his face.

Another half-track rolled in . . . more doughboys dismounted. . . . I got the wireless set out of my crutch, pulled my head free and crawled down to the ground. . . . Running from girder to girder behind the Americans, I got across to Odlebog. He was dead. No more would he sniff the corn-store at Silberplatz. Vacancy for warehouse manager at Gradheim and Koch. . . . I eased the contract from his fingers and searched his pockets till I found my cheque. No point in leaving signed cheques lying about the battlefield. I tore up both pieces of paper, tossed them into the Rhine and set off back across the sleepers the way I had come.

And that was how I captured the Ludendorff Bridge at Remagen, the only bridge across the Rhine that was taken intact.

Chapter Nineteen

You have wondered, no doubt, why our soldiers do not smile when you wave your hands, or say "Good Morning" in the streets or play with the children. . . . Our soldiers have seen their comrades shot down, their homes in ruins, their wives and children hungry. They have seen terrible things in many countries where your rulers took the war . . . every nation is responsible for its rulers and while they were successful you cheered and laughed. That is why our soldiers do not smile at you.

F-M. Viscount Montgomery of Alamein—Message to the German People 10th June 1945

If left to himself the British soldier will soon be on the best terms with the local population. Unfortunately this time he was not left to himself and all sorts of regulations about non-fraternization with the German people were issued . . . our troops were prevented from getting to know ordinary, decent families in an open, normal way and were driven to consorting with the lowest types of German women. In spite of the non-fraternization rules I was determined somehow to make our occupation as palatable as possible for the local inhabitants . . . I therefore ordered all units in my corps to do everything they could to help the German children . . .

Lt. Gen. Sir Brian Horrocks
A Full Life

By the time I caught up with the Musketeers they had joined the British Second Army which was still regrouping on the east bank of the Lower Rhine. My chaps in Twelve Platoon were so pleased to see me that they all went out on the night of my arrival and got drunk. Although some of them were undeniably edgy with hangover next morning, I

[247]

felt justified in overlooking their excesses since my popularity was to blame for their jubilation. I had to disappoint them, too, by announcing that they would not, after all, be spearheading the Allied advance across the Rhine. It had been ordained that the Division would be held in reserve during the river assault ready to pass through the bridgehead when it was secure and strike out into the Westphalian plain.

The Regiment was settled in Gretmund, thirty miles back from the Rhine, safely out of range of the enemy but uncomfortably close to Army Headquarters. The farther you got back from the line, the stricter became the observance of the decrees against fraternization. Around the Gretmund district they had special M. P. patrols to detect and discourage any illegal looks, smiles, or unseemly badinage between soldiers and civilians.

The Army Group Commander issued a personal letter to each officer and man under His command explaining why He had sent the Germans to Coventry. It was printed on a card which could be carried in the battle-dress pocket and I found it most helpful. Whenever I was tempted to pat the head of a Boche child or to relax my frown at its starving mother, I would take the card from my pocket and strengthen my spirit from His words. I also read it out to Twelve Platoon daily at first parade stressing the Commander's points that "if we mix freely with the Germans, go to their homes, dance with their girls and so on, it would be resented by our own families in England and by millions of people who had suffered under the Gestapo. When we first enter Germany, it will be too soon to distinguish between good and bad Germans, we must therefore hold back and not fraternize till we can see our way clear."

"And so, men," I would exhort them each morning, "let each of us resolve that this day we shall not fraternize."

"We don't want to fraternize 'em," whispered Private Drogue. "We just want to f— 'em."

[248]

Which jocular remark, I'm afraid, summed up the general attitude of the Musketeers. After the free and easy relations we had enjoyed with the Italians, all ranks found it doubly difficult to observe the prohibition of intercourse with the German people. And I do mean intercourse.

We had about three weeks in and around Gretmund and the ugly head of my old enemy reared itself once again. I've never felt quite sure what the curse of Cain was, but if it was loose women then he'd have been at home in Twelve Platoon. In Africa, Italy, and Greece I had been forced to fight a running battle with concupiscence, and now Germany was to give me no relief. I had, fortunately, no daunting madames to contend with this time since the houses of ill-fame in the town were carefully watched by the non-fraternization patrols and for a soldier to set nose through the bead curtains was to invite immediate retribution.

The good-time girls of Gretmund, therefore, had to operate on a lone she-wolf basis. The official anti-civilian defences were most vulnerable to such individual infiltration and the actual separation of the British soldier from the female German called for much diligence at platoon commander level. The women were naturally cunning, the men hopping alive with lustful ingenuity, and I had to exercise a high degree of personal vigilance to ensure that Twelve Platoon maintained the standard of misogynous discipline desired by the Supreme Commander.

In Gretmund we were billeted in the remnant of a bombed hotel. The habitable wing had housed the kitchen and servants quarters and was a regular warren of interlocking rooms and rambling corridors. I found at the very outset that I could not rely on the wholehearted support of my N. C. O.'s in the enforcement of our segregation orders. On the first evening I placed them on watch at strategic points of entry to the billets and was bitterly disappointed when I made my snap inspection to find Corporal Dooley in trouserless fraternization on the basement steps with Little Jo-Jo, a strawberry blonde well up on my list of undesirables.

"I trust, sir," he said, shirt-tails flapping as he came to the salute, "that you'll not be thinking anything untoward. 'Tis a button come off me trousers, sir, and this lady offered to sew it on."

Corporal Hink had retreated from his position at the wash-house door and was undressing a brunette called Loreli in the larder. He said she looked Greek to him and he was prudently searching her skirt for weapons. In the reception hall Corporal Globe was recumbent on the key counter with Red Marlene. He claimed that he was getting something out of her eye when he came over faint. The greatest blow awaited my return to operational headquarters in the kitchen, where I found Sergeant Transom wrapped in the blonde vastness of Big Magda, and so absorbed in his work that he did not even hear my approach. Discreet coughing gained not a flicker of response from either party, and I had to poke him twice on the shoulder with my swagger stick before I could gain his attention.

"I was trying to tire her out, sir," he said, "so that she'd not have the urge to go worrying the men no more tonight. It was a personal sacrifice as you might say, sir, for the protection of our subordinates."

I told him that no matter what his motives may be it was only common politeness for a senior N. C. O. engaged as he was to make pause in his passion when addressed by a commissioned officer. The flesh, I knew, was weak but there was no call for discourtesy.

I did not feel that I should put all my N. C. O.'s on charge together without first discussing the matter with Major Ark-dust. He was rather hard to get hold of at that period because most of his time was spent with Colonel Plaster and the adjutant in pursuit of a certain cache of Nazi-hidden hock which was apparently the Montepico '92 of the Rhineland.

Although, when I did catch him, I explained that the Army Group Commander's personal orders were in breach, he refused to accept charges against my four N. C. O.'s.

"We've still got to fight the blasted war, Goodbody," he said, "in spite of the Army Group Commander's puritan upbringing. I can't afford to have all you N. C. O.'s under arrest for fondling *fräuleins*. Do you think I want to assault the Rhine with you all alone in charge of Twelve Platoon?"

I could see his point. Even though I was senior platoon commander, I could not fight my command in battle without any supporting N. C. O.'s. Not for long, anyway.

"And furthermore," he said, "the colonel has made it plain that while this non-fraternization edict requires his obedience, it does not command his sympathy. He will thank no one for bringing N. C. O.'s up on orders about it. I have, therefore, decided that antifrat discipline is a matter for platoon commanders. The campaign for the sexual separation of British soldiers from any available woman is henceforth a personal matter between the Army Group Commander and yourself."

I saluted smartly and told him how I appreciated the trust he was displaying in my judgment by devolving so important a discipline matter to my level. It was now a private battle between me and Twelve Platoon.

As a first step, I strengthened the defences. I had all the windows on the ground floor filled in with sandbags and nailed up every door but the main entrance. At the top of the building was an attic room that ran from back to front. There were windows in three walls and it commanded views of all approaches to the hotel. I moved into this room and made it my personal headquarters. I laid trip-wires at night and connected them to the suite of servants' bells on the wall. From a glance at which red dodger was down I could tell immediately the quarter of the enemy's attack. I could reach the kitchen in twenty-five seconds flat by means of the dumbwaiter. It was rather cramped crouched up in a lift built for nothing larger than a turkey, but the discomfort was worth it when I debouched the first night and caught Private Drogue and Black Bertha sporting amorously on the pastry slab.

The main stairs provided a simple alarm route to the front of my fortress and my lightning way to the back was down a rope ladder which I fixed from a landing window to the roof of the washhouse. It was a tricky descent, but it enabled me to surprise within a single hour, Private Gripweed grappled to Gretchen against the garden wall, and Private Spool and Fat Elsa twined in a wrestling hold of such ingenuity that he pulled a hip ligament getting out.

I introduced a system of fraternization fines payable to the Platoon Benevolent Fund. It was a shilling for a smile at the enemy, two shillings for a kind word, half a crown for a charitable waste of Army rations, or aiding the entry of a female to billets, five bob for petting or kissing, and half if copped in full penetration. This fund mounted steadily, and I made a fine sweep on the third night when I detected Corporal Hink's secret tart tunnel through the coke chute and nabbed his whole section romping erotically, turn and turn about with the dresden-sized Sukie, tiny Tilda, and Lotte and Lisa, the sixteen-year-old nymphomaniac twins. They were the only Gretmund geishas small enough to get through the coal hole. I thought at first torch light that Hink had got hold of coloured women, but quickly realized that it was merely the coal dust which had blackened their buttocks.

I had barbed wire stuffed down all chimneys after Little Jo-Jo, at Corporal Globe's admitted instigation, was trapped at midnight by the bend at the bottom of the main flue. She was caught with head and shoulders up the throat and her bottom half safely out and over the kitchen range. I was gratified to note that Globe still had some spark of English decency unsubmerged by lust, since he made no attempt to take advantage of the girl in her unfortunate but provocative position.

[252]

My faith in my fellow men was disagreeably jolted when, after a buzz on my wires at three o'clock in the morning, I raced to the washhouse to find Private Clapper unbuttoned from ear to ear, *in flagrante delicto* with Red Marlene. When I had relieved him of half a bar I asked him what sort of reward this was for my efforts to ensure the marital fidelity of Mrs. Clapper.

"I'm very sorry, sir," he said, adjusting his dress before leaving, "I just don't know what came over me. It occurred, sir, in a blinding moment of ungovernable passion."

I advised him to take more exercise and avoid highly spiced food in the future. One hundred per cent fit though I was, the nightly strain of watching for the red dodgers, humping in the dumbwaiter, and racing down rope ladders began to tell on me. Twelve Platoon fought back doggedly. As I sealed one loophole of lechery, they devised another. Alerted one night to the larder, I pulled at the rope for the dumbwaiter to find that it was weighing a ton. It was vertical tug-of-war all the way, and when I finally got it to the top, prespiration dripping and blisters newly bulging, I found Private Drogue and Lorelei coiled up inside in a mating position of truly embryonic economy. If I had not seen it myself I would have never believed it possible for a pair of adult humans so to perform within the confines of a dumbwaiter. I let go the rope in surprise and God knows what new depths of satisfaction were plumbed by Lorelei when the lift hit bottom.

I lost more ground the next night when I found Corporal Dooley helping Big Magda to climb *up* my emergency rope ladder. Unfortunately for her, it was not built to stand her weight and with the warwail of the Valkyrie she went seat first through the roof of the washhouse. Her bruises kept her out of business for a week.

In the face of these setbacks, I was relieved when Major Arkdust announced that a platoon was to be detailed to guard a landing strip from possible flying Werewolves. The strip was fifteen miles north of Gretmund in the middle of a miniature Salisbury Plain and I jumped at the chance to get Twelve Platoon out of town. We left next day and for the last five miles we rolled on a single line track through a desolation of peat bog and starving bracken. At the landing strip there was just one asbestos hangar and not another habitation as far as the eye could see. It was an ideal spot for non-fraternization.

The chaps were not too happy at first, but I drew up a busy schedule of airstrip defence exercises, cross-country marches and weapon-training quizzes, and after a week of the simple life their spirits seemed to recover. They all slept in the body of the hangar and I had a pleasant billet in the office rooms along one side. We didn't see much of the colonel or Major Arkdust because they were still busy hunting the hock, but the padre called on us in the wilderness. It was the day after his visit that my three corporals came to see me.

"I've come to ask you, sir, on behalf of the men," said Corporal Dooley, "if we could have your support in a little Christian endeavour?"

I reflected what a leveller of the lascivious is fresh air and physical exertion.

"Certainly," I said. "What is this endeavour?"

"It said in yesterday's battalion orders that the fraternization rules are now slightly relaxed and that the Corps Commander wished us to do all we can to help the German children."

"That's right."

The Corps Commander seemed to lean a little towards the sympathies of Colonel Plaster. While urging all units to maintain rigid adult non-fraternization, he now requested those who were in a position to do so, to help the children by running youth clubs, camps, sports, and similar festivities.

"The padre talked to us about it, sir, and he says there's a convent orphanage in Gretmund with loads of kids that want looking after. We can't run no sports nor youth clubs out here in this no-man's-land, but the men have talked it over among themselves and they would like to devote the Platoon Benevolent Fund to laying on a tea party one day for a load of kids from the orphanage."

"Most commendable, Corporal Dooley. The Fund is very affluent at the moment due, as you know, to certain unfortunate incidents at our Gretmund billet. The application of such monies to so worthy a cause would be most appropriate."

"That's just what the boys felt, sir." He hung his head and beat a penitent fist over his heart. "The wages of sin should be devoted to making poor little children happy."

"Filling their poor little stomachs," said Corporal Hink.

"Bringing a smile to their poor little faces," said Corporal Globe.

"The padre's off on leave tomorrow," went on Corporal Dooley, "but before he goes he's going to arrange it with the Mother Superior for a party of the kids to come here for a big blowout next Tuesday afternoon. And knowing how kind-hearted you are, sir, Sergeant Transom has already fixed it with the M. T. Sergeant for us to have a three-tonner to bring them out."

The Platoon flung themselves with great gusto into the arrangements for the party. Trestle tables appeared, clothed with flags of all nations, red and white flannelette festoons garlanded the girders, teapots, cutlery, and crockery were magically scrounged, N. A. A. F. I. chocolate and sweet rations were pooled, paper hats were pasted up and under the direction of Corporal Globe, piemaker by profession, cakes, jellies, and corned-beef sandwiches were produced in profusion. A small stage was erected, auditions were held, games tried out, and entertainments rehearsed. I had written my speech of welcome and was running through that hilarious version of "Widecombe Fair" which invariably brought the house down at the Philatelic Society Socials—I put *real* names of people present in place of Daniel Whiddon, Harry Hawk and the others—when I suddenly remembered that the colonel had ordered an officers' meeting for that Tuesday afternoon to deliver his latest Campaign Summary. I would have to be in Gretmund till late evening and would not be able to attend the party. I took off my funny nose and broke the sad news to Sergeant Transom.

"That will take the gilt off the gingerbread for everybody, sir," he said in disappointment, "but it can't be helped. All the arrangements are too far gone now to alter the day, I'm afraid."

I arrived in Gretmund on Tuesday just in time to see the three-tonner pulling out. Corporal Dooley was driving with a black-habited nun beside him. Two more escorting nuns sat on guard at either side of the tailboard and a row of happy little faces peered over it like festive, female Chads, waving streamers and trailing balloons. Shrill, excited cheering came out from the rest of them underneath the canopy, and I waved my cap merrily until they were out of sight. Half an hour later we were all gathered at Battalion Headquarters when the adjutant brought a message from the colonel cancelling the meeting. He was out on a special reconnaissance and could not now get back that afternoon. Privately, it was rumoured, he had come upon a really hot lead to that cache of transcendental hock. Much as I enjoyed the colonel's Campaign Summaries, I was pleased at the cancellation. I would be able to do "Widecombe Fair" for the kids, after all. I was making hotfoot for my jeep when Captain Crocker nobbled me about alleged inaccuracies in my last long and short pants return. It took me most of an hour to explain my infallible triple-entry system to his satisfaction and it was after four when I finally pulled into the airstrip. The party was in full swing as I opened the side door from my office into the hangar . . .

I staggered back, concussed with horror. . . . The Gramophone was booming, Corporal Dooley was singing "I'm in the Mood for Love," and two nuns were up on the stage doing a striptease act!

Their robes flowed off like blackout curtains on Victory Night while, in the body of the kirk, girls in school blazers, girls in gym slips, girls in baby-doll frocks, girls in pigtails and ankle socks danced cheek-to-cheek and thigh-to-thigh with my soldiery. . . . They were tall girls for their age . . . they filled their childish clothing overwell . . . they wore lipstick, eye-shadow and mascara beneath the ribbons in their hair. . . . One of the nuns was down to the buff above the waist, and I recognized Big Magda . . . and there was Lorelei, dressed for kindergarten and rolling her hips like rubber under the happy hands of Private Spool . . . Little Jo-Jo, in baby's bonnet and indecent rompers, was glued to Corporal Hink like a female flypaper . . . Red Marlene, bulging tight-laced in Tyrolean shorts, and Sergeant Transom, swayed as one body and drank together from the same teacup . . . Lotte and Lisa were sitting this one out, enjoying Swedish massage from either hand of Private Drogue . . . Tilda was saving her sandals by dancing with legs twined about the waist of Corporal Globe . . . Gretchen, dressed as a fairy, lay stretched across the quivering knees of Private Clapper . . . Fat Elsa, a bodice-bursting Red Riding Hood, squealed in the pinching grasp of Private Gripweed, and the remaining nun, coif off to reveal Black Bertha, leaned back in her chair and drank red wine from the spout of a teapot.

Bottles were stacked along the table . . . cigarettes spilled among the balloons . . . and at the nearest end to the stage, six little children perhaps nine or ten years old, the bright faces I had seen above the tailboard, waved their streamers in time to the music and cheered shrilly as the second nun got down to skin level and Corporal Dooley, looping an arm about each, swung them with him in a whooping can-can!

"Stop!" I cried, leaping forward like the avenging angel. "Stop his orgy! Cease that bacchanal!"

They froze like statues in mid-debauch, a guilty tableau by

[257]

Hogarth. . . . The main doors opened and Colonel Plaster came in. . . .

"Ah, there you are, Goodbody," he said. "Just come to see you. Hear you've got a children's party . . . God bless my soul! What's this?"

"Just the children's party, sir," said Sergeant Transom, unpeeling himself from Red Marlene. "And . . . er . . . and one or two of the young mothers to help things along."

The nuns hastily resumed the veil, Lotte and Lisa pulled down their gym slips, Tilda unwound from Corporal Globe, Gripweed let his last handful of Fat Elsa slap back into place. An uneasy silence came over all.

Colonel Plaster looked slowly around the hangar, brushing up his moustache querulously.

"By George!" he cried at last, smiting me on the shoulder. "By George! Goodbody, but I never thought you had it in you. All that teetotal, straitlaced stuff you put on. And look at this . . . this . . . blasted saturnalia!"

"I'm extremely sorry, sir, I thought it was going to be a proper children's party . . ."

"That's what it is, man. Don't let's have any misunderstanding about it." He waved an authoritative hand about the company. "As fine a lot of children as I've seen ever. And don't let me hear anyone say different. First-class idea and a first-class party. Sergeant Transom . . ."

"Sir."

"Have you got anywhere here that might be . . . er . . . well . . . a bit private, you know! I'd like to have a few words with one or two of the children. By myself, of course . . . put them at their ease that way, you know. Important that we get to know how they feel, what?"

"Yes, sir! Right away, sir. Mr. Goodbody's office, sir. Just in there. Only one door and I'll be on it myself."

"Good show, Sergeant. Now, let's see . . ." He squared his shoulders and flexed his legs in a policeman's bend. "I'll have

[258]

a word with that little girl there . . ." He pointed to the raven-haired Lorelei. ". . . and that one there." Sukie bowed her golden head and smiled dutifully.

He waved to the company as he went into my office, followed by the two girls.

"Righto, the rest of you. Carry on with the party. Enjoy yourselves. Get on with the games."

"Would you like me to come and take notes, sir?" I asked, anxious to be of assistance.

I don't think he heard my offer because he slammed the door quickly and shot home the bolt. I turned to Sergeant Transom.

"However liberally the colonel may choose to view this disgraceful affair, Sergeant," I said with the utmost severity, "there is one thing for which I will never be able to forgive you. . . . It is bad enough to abuse my absence by arranging this frightful orgy with these dreadful women. But to bring along those little children as camouflage and to force them to witness your debauchery is quite unspeakable. I shudder to think what appalling, moral damage you have done to their young minds."

"They won't come to no harm, sir. They're the oldest of the lot. They ain't kids. They're midgets."

"Midgets?"

"Yes, sir. Tom Thumb-size tarts. Refugees from a very fancy house in Cologne catering for circuses, wealthy dwarfs and fullgrown gentlemen with curious fads."

In view of the colonel's last order I had no alternative but to carry on the party. I insisted that if it were a children's party they should play children's games. I made them play oranges and lemons, nuts-and-may, and other running-up-and-down diversions which I devised to drain off the sexual urge. I avoided any pastimes of an inflammatory nature, such as postman's knock or sardines, and took the precaution of dividing them into a boys' team and a girls' team. And when

[259]

they sank, at last, exhausted on their seats, I went up on to the stage and gave them my hilarious version of "Widecombe Fair."

As I was finishing the last chorus, Colonel Plaster came out of the office. I stepped down and escorted him to the door.

"Never been so surprised by a chap in all my life, Goodbody," he said. "You're a blasted dark horse and no mistake. Midgets, too, they tell me, you've got here . . . midgets, mind you . . . they must be quite an experience. . . . By George! What a damned sly dog you turned out to be."

He patted me confidentially on the shoulder just where that third pip would lie.

"I'm seeing you in a new light, my boy, from this day on. Never know but that there might be something for you shortly . . . providing of course that you don't fall down on security or anything like that. Got to know when to keep your mouth shut, you know, if you're going to get on. Not a word about my visit here today. Not a word, you know, to anybody."

He laid a silent finger to the side of his nose.

"You may rely on me, sir."

I could see from the corner of my imagination that captaincy glinting on my epaulette.

"And I'll be back to see you in the morning, Goodbody. Got a lead that damned hock may be somewhere on the airstrip. That's why I came to see you. . . . Good-bye . . . and get those children back before dark."

He let in the clutch and pulled away. Sukie and Lorelei ran alongside his jeep as far as they could blowing kisses and waving him farewell.

Chapter Twenty

We find the Russians as individuals easy to deal with. The Russians undoubtedly like the American people. They like the United States . . . above all, they want to maintain friendly relations with us . . . they are a tenacious, determined people who think and act just like you and I do. . . .

THE WHITE HOUSE
PAPERS OF HARRY HOPKINS—
August 1st, 1945

In his generous instincts, in his love of laughter, in his devotion to his comrades, and in his healthy, direct outlook on the affairs of workaday life, the ordinary Russian seems to me to bear a marked similarity to what we call the "average American."

GEN. DWIGHT D. EISENHOWER
Crusade in Europe, 1948

EVER TRUE TO TRADITION, Twelve Platoon waited till the engineers had built their bridge, and on All-Fools Day, 1945, walked dry-shod across the Rhine. We pressed on behind the armour for the Elbe and would have got there a fortnight before we did if, once again, the towns *en route* had not been so over-bombed as to be almost impassable. We made the river line by the end of April, the German resistance dwindling steadily as we advanced. When Hitler killed himself on the last day of the month the collapse was complete and we drove unhindered for the Baltic coast to seal off the Danish peninsula. Unhindered, that is, by enemy aggression, but impeded at every turn by vast field-grey herds of surrendering Wehrmacht, horse and cart convoys of released and joyful prisoners of war, and packs of drunken, displaced persons, wild with liberty, howling in unknown languages, and tirelessly seeking fresh bellyfuls of booze.

As we threaded our way towards Wissmar we learnt that the Russians were advancing from Rostock, thirty miles farther along the coast. Anxious to avoid starting another war with the Russians so soon after we had finished one with the Germans, the Army Group Commander issued special orders about the drill to be adopted on meeting our gallant Allies. Because of the language difficulty, radio was no use and indiscriminate patrolling would obviously court trouble. It was laid down, therefore, that when contact with the Russians was imminent, both sides should halt, the commanders meet and arrange as best they could clear-cut boundaries and junction lines. With so historic a rendezvous ahead of us, I felt the occasion warranted a special address to my troops.

"We are coming, chaps," I said, "to the end of the road. Across the world together we have trod the stony path from first defeat to final victory. Through Africa, Italy, Greece, France, and Germany we have hit the Boche for six, sent him back on his heeels, dealt him knock-out blows and driven him into the sea. We have had our ups and our downs, our good times, and our bad times, but always we have fought through together to ultimate victory. And now that the Great Umpire Up Above will soon be calling Close of Play in this Second World War, I want you to know how grateful I am to have had the good fortune to command such a fine body of men. There has been no happier band of brothers in arms than good old Twelve Platoon. Without your courage, your true British grit, your steadfast devotion to duty, I could have done nothing. We commanders can only plan and scheme, order and inspire, and use our brains, training, and God-given ability to launch you chaps into battle on the best possible wicket. The victories we have gained have been due

[262]

just as much to your noble efforts as to my tactical leadership. It has been a great privilege to have led you all in the fight to free the Soul of Europe from the Heel of the Aggressor. On behalf of His Majesty the King and the people of Britain I give you the thanks of a simple soldier-man. Thank you, men ... thank you ... one and all ..."

I allowed my voice to choke a little on the second thank you.

"Stop," said Private Drogue, blowing his nose like a foghorn. "You're breaking my bleeeding heart."

"But now that we have won the war," I continued. "We must be sure to win the peace. And peace in Europe in the years to come will rest upon amity and good feeling between the British and the Russians. Sometime today or tomorrow we shall be joining hands with our gallant Soviet Allies. First impressions are always significant. This time they will be of vital importance to world peace. I look to Twelve Platoon to take the Russians to their hearts and show them that goodwill and bonhomie for which Tommy Atkins is famed the world over."

"Ruddy Russians," said Corporal Globe. "They was behind them perishing ELAS in Greece."

"Bleeding Bolshies," said Corporal Hink. "I seen 'em on the pictures. Rasputin and all that lot."

"I recommend to you the sentiments of our most Noble Ally, the lately mourned and sadly lost President Roosevelt who knew the Russians so well. He found that as individuals they are easy to deal with, that they undoubtedly like the people of the United States with whom, above all, they want friendly relations, and that they are a tenacious, determined people who think and act just like any ordinary American. So, you see, we have it from the President himself that the Russians are no different to the Americans. We have always got on well with the Americans. Therefore we shall get on well with the Russians ..."

[263]

"I never liked no bloody Yanks, neither," said Private Spool. "Hope to Gawd the Russians don't come chewing bubble gum."

"And in further recommendation," I emphasized, "let me tell you the views of our Supreme Commander, General Eisenhower himself, who knows just as many Russians as President Roosevelt. He finds from his experience that, in his generous instincts, in his love of laughter, in his devotion to his comrades, in his healthy direct outlook on the affairs of workaday life, the ordinary Russian seems to bear a marked similarity to what we call an average American . . ."

"Roll on my healthy direct outlook on the affairs of workaday life," said Corporal Dooley. "And I'll see you down the drugstore, Voroshilov."

"French, Germans, Yanks, Russians," said Private Drogue darkly. "Sod 'em all."

"It is clear," I went on, "that our American friends are confident of winning friends and influencing people in Russia. They will clearly extend their triumph of war into a victory of peace. We must do the same. During the next few days, each and every one of us in good old Twelve Platoon must regard himself as a Spearhead Ambassador for Anglo-Soviet Harmony. Each must extend the hand of greeting to every Russian soldier he meets. Warrior saluting warrior with battle nobly done, East meeting West in triumphant *camaraderie*, each smile, each word, each rough, soldierly backslap forging another link in the new chain of friendship between the British Commonwealth and All the Russias. In our hands lies the key to Peace in Europe in Our Time . . ."

"I wish I'd known," said Corporal Dooley, "I'd have brought me umbrella."

On May 2nd we were in sight of the Baltic when the order came to stop. The river Lenlo was fixed as the eastern boundary of the Musketeers and Twelve Platoon was settled in a farmhouse overlooking the bridge on the road from Klaghaus

[264]

to Rostock. Obedient to the Army Commander's behest I had prepared myself for the situation. I had obtained a large Union Jack, fashioned a Red Flag from a captured Father Christmas overcoat and made two large sign boards showing a white arrow on a black ground.

Leaving Sergeant Transom in charge of the billet I went down alone to the bridge with my boundary equipment. I wanted to get the border line clearly established before the Russians arrived so that there would be no trouble about demarcation. I was anxious also to handle the first exchanges myself, thus ensuring mutual goodwill at the outset and avoiding the danger of any undiplomatic subordinates getting things off on the wrong foot.

I painted a broad white line across the middle of the bridge, mounting the Union Jack and one western-pointing arrow on our side, and placing the Red Flag with the other arrow at the eastern end. I was just in time. The historic moment was at hand. Around the bend in the road, two hundred yards away, came a Russian infantry patrol. There were about thirty of them, squat slit-eyed men with Mongolian features, each carrying a sack over his shoulder and an automatic weapon in his hands. Three were wobbling forward on bicycles, yellow teeth biting lower lips in concentration, battling hazardously and grimly as children on their first two-wheelers. Their forearms glittered in the sunshine and I thought they were wearing some form of limb armour. When they came closer I saw that every man was wearing ranks of wristwatches up to each elbow. One had a grandmother clock on his back held by a thong around his temples. The cyclists fell off here and there, but clambered solemnly back into the saddle each time like determined, inscrutable chimpanzees.

"Welcome, *tovarich*," I cried, raising my clenched fist in the Communist salute. "Long Live Stalin! Long Live Churchill! Three cheers for All the Russias. On behalf of the Allied Forces in Western Europe, I salute you!"

They said not a word of acknowledgement or congratulation, but marched silently on. I advanced to meet them holding out my hands in affectionate hospitality.

"Welcome, *tovarich!* Greetings to one and all in the gallant Red Army! In the name of the common people of Britain, I salute you!"

They swarmed about me, chrome-laced forearms flashing, eyes button-black and expressionless, brown dirt crusted on flat, Asiatic jowls. Suddenly a myriad hands shot out and held me everywhere, gripping my arms, ankles, and shoulders, plucking at every slack in my battle dress.

"Welcome, *tovarich!*" I said encouragingly. "Long Live Marshal Stalin! Long Live Timoshenko! U.S.S.R. hurrah!"

The Tartar shaking my left hand took off my wristwatch and added it to his collection.

"Ug," he said. "Ug."

The Afghan greeting my right hand whipped out my fountain pen and bit it. Ink flowed like blue blood down his chin.

"Ug-Ug," he said.

"Now, look here," I protested. "I am a British officer. I am your gallant ally. . . . Side by side we have fought against the Nazi hordes . . ."

Fingers ran into my pockets, my beret vanished from my head, boots came unlaced and jerked off my feet.

"Ug," said the holder of the left.

"Ug-Ug," said the winner of the right.

"Really!" I cried. "We are *tovarichs* . . . friends . . . allies. Where is your officer?"

I tried to get up but a hundred fingers held me back. The cold road prickled my feet as my socks were whipped away.

"Help!" I yelled. "Help! Twelve Platoon! Rally on me!"

My commands were muffled as, baffled by the mystery of buttons, four hands tore my jacket straight up over my head and yanked it inside-out along my arms.

"Ug . . . Ug . . . Ug!" grunted the sleeve-strainers. Fingers

[266]

probed the elastic novelty of my braces, stretching them out fit for Tammany Hall, sliding the loops over my shoulders . . . my trousers began slithering down my legs . . . I pumped out my stomach as bulbous as a Japanese wrestler, fighting the waistband every inch of the way.

"Help! Help!" I shouted. "Twelve Platoon! Rally! rally, rally!"

Answering yells echoed down the road and the clatter of British hobnails came as music to my ears.

"Ug!" snapped someone commandingly. "Ug-ug-ug!" All the hands lifted in unison, and I was swung up in the air to be held horizontally above their flat, black heads. The levitation caught my stomach off guard and my trousers flowed away. The cortège turned and trotted back the way they had come, bearing me aloft, stark and stiff in my underwear like a corpse looking for a coffin. They had almost made it to the bend when good old Twelve Platoon caught up with them.

"Put him down, you perishing Bolshies!" shouted Sergeant Transom yanking back my left elbow-carrier by the scruff of his grandmother clock.

"Let's have you," bellowed Corporal Dooley, laying about him with his belt. "Pinch a platoon commander from the Musketeers, would you? Thieving ruddy Communists!"

And the rest of the platoon pitched into the little Mongol men with boot and buckle and belt. . . . My bearers dropped me in self-defence and I rolled over the tarmac and into a dry ditch . . . thistles prickled uncomfortably through my pants, cellular and holly branches taloned my vest. . . . From the way they were whooping and the bottles some were wielding, my command had found the vino once again . . . wrestling with the Russians, fighting each other as partners ran out, they made a Saturday night at Blaydon Races right there on the high road to Rostock.

I untangled my vest from the holly bush and regained my feet.

"Stop!" I yelled, flailing my arms commandingly. "In the name of Anglo-Soviet cooperation and the postwar peace of Europe, stop this unseemly brawl!"

Both sides looked up in surprise . . . took off their strangle-holds for a second . . . stopped pummelling momentarily. Then the Russians broke away and scurried like black mice off down the road. Sergeant Transom pursued the last of them for twenty yards, kicking him up the rump. Private Drogue hurled rocks till they were out of range. Corporal Hink hit one on the back of the head with a long-range bottle. The glass shattered but the recipient never even slackened his stride.

"Saucy bastards! Looting off Twelve Platoon!" said Sergeant Transom in horrified tones. "Did you ever? What a dead flaming liberty! Pinching the clobber off a live Musketeer. . . . Here you are, sir . . . there's your blouse and trousers back."

"Thank you," I said, feeling much better with my legs covered. "It was good of you to come to my rescue when you did. But I must deprecate your use of violence against our Russian allies. You should have followed the example of the Metropolitan Police and used no more force than was necessary to detain them. Had you done so and given me an opportunity to address them quietly I feel sure I could have turned the incident to the benefit of Anglo-Russian relations. As it is, I fear that your infliction of unjustified personal violence on these comrades in arms smaller in stature than yourselves may well have poisoned their minds against the British for ever. By punching and kicking them after they had released me you may well have jeopardized peace in Europe in years to come. Don't think I'm ungrateful, but . . ."

"That's all they understand, them Ruskies," said Sergeant Transom. "Just like the Wogs or the Gungas. Nothing they respect like brute force. A good old kick up the arse or a clip round the ear, and they know you mean business."

[268]

"Your outlook is quite outdated," I said. "Those unfortunate men may now be driven to attack us in revenge for the indignities they have suffered. As President Roosevelt so wisely said, only by allaying their suspicions and showing the open hand of friendship can we win the goodwill of the Russian people . . ."

"Here's your socks . . . and your right boot. Those Bolshies have made off with your left one . . ." He stopped and pointed up the road. "Aye-aye, lads! Get set . . . looks as if them sawn-off Caucasians are coming back for another barney."

Around the bend came the Russian patrol once more. At their head walked one with stripes on his arm, bearing before him in one hand my left boot and in the other, my wristwatch. Their faces wreathed in smiles, becking and nodding as affectionately as car-passing Royalty, they marched up to the bridge.

"Ug . . . Ug . . . Ug-Ug!" snapped the leader. His men halted. He came forward, beaming like first dividend, and presented the boot and the watch to Sergeant Transom. As the sergeant took the offerings the Russian clasped him to his bosom and kissed him three times on each cheek.

"Ug . . ." he boomed admiringly. "Ug . . . *Tovarich* . . . Ug-Ug-Ug!"

He flourished his cap and his followers cheered in unison.

"Ug-Ug! *Tovarish!* Ug-Ug-Ug!"

They took their sacks from their shoulders and produced bottles of every alcoholic shape.

"*Tovarich!*" cried Sergeant Transom. "Good health, matey, and Ug-Ug-Ug!"

Twelve Platoon echoed his sentiments and after boisterous Anglo-Russian kissing all round settled in to punish the bottles with the Siberians. Sergeant Transom, arms linked and brandy flask shared with the headman, came over and gave me my left boot.

[269]

"There you are, sir," he said. "I told you there was nothing a Russian respects like a good old boot up the arse."

"Thank you, Sergeant. But I do assure you that such action is quite out of keeping with modern concepts of international relations and the American way of diplomacy . . ."

But before I could finish he was borne off by his companions to the centre of the bridge where, to the music of an Ukrainian concertina, Privates Drogue and Spool were on mobile hunkers Cossack-dancing with a pair of pig-tailed Tartars. As I bent to pull on my boot, Private Clapper came over.

"Begging your pardon, sir," he said, "but while the others are suitably engaged might I have a few words with you."

"Certainly, Clapper," I said pulling tight the laces. "Is it Mrs. Clapper again?"

"I'm afraid so, sir."

I stood up and straightened my uniform. This was familiar country. This was my type of war.

"We'll walk up to the farm together, Clapper, and you can tell me all about it. Now let me see . . . we left Mrs. Clapper, if I remember rightly, as an uninsured, vegetarian, swimming bath attendant?"

"That's right, sir. And it's that swimming bath what's caused all the trouble. There's this health-and-strength bloke gets in there three times a week, bringing his own dumbbells, turning somersaults over the springboards, and body-building himself like Hercules' big brother. Struts up and down the side of the bath flexing his deltoids and blowing up his triceps till Mrs. Clapper just don't know which way to look. First off, he used to follow her about on her ablutionary duties and kept trying to back her up into empty cubicles. Eighteen stone of Mr. Universe he's got there, sir, and that's more nor her poor little seven-and-half stone of flesh and blood can stand."

"You don't mean, Clapper," I said "that he's . . . er . . . he's

[270]

wreaking his wicked will on her in a public cubicle of her own swimming bath?"

"She wouldn't let him, sir. Not my little girl. She hollered for the Superintendent, my mum says. So now that over-grown Tarzan has taken to picking her up bodily and carry-ing her down to the used towel store and having his huge hoggins off her in there three times a week. The poor little kid's right puny on just them vegetables all the time, my mum says, and ain't no longer got the power to resist him. . . . Now is it right, sir, that's all I want to know, while a man's away fighting to liberate Europe from the Yoke, for bleeding street-corner Samsons to keep on stuffing it up his wife in a used towel store? That's all I'm asking sir, is it?"

"I quite take your point, Clapper. We must not be deterred by disappointment. Let us take this rebuff as a spur to further ingenuity. Now let us consider where to find the sexual Achilles heel of the modern Atlas. These muscle-men, I have found, are usually terrified by any mental pursuit which demands exercise of the brain. Now, it seems to me, if we could find some suitable course at adult evening classes for Mrs. Clapper to take up, we might well provide her with a line of intellectual conversation which would rapidly frighten off her gymnastic persecutor. . . . Now let me see. . . . What about the Early English Poets . . . quotations from Caedmon or Langland have ever been lowering. . . . Or the Meaning of Art . . . verbal descriptions of modern paintings can be most bewildering to the predominantly muscular?"

"I'm afraid, sir, Mrs. Clapper never was no good at the drawing."

"Never mind. We must persevere. We'll find something to suit her, never fear. . . ."

As we walked together towards the farmhouse we left Twelve Platoon behind on the bridge, Corporal Dooley and some grandson of Ghengis Khan in loving embrace and sing-ing "Otchi Chernia," Private Drogue and Spool fan-dancing

[271]

lasciviously with my two allied flags, Corporals Hink and Globe, with four poker-faced Uzbekistanis, playing ring-o'-roses round the grandmother clock, and Sergeant Transom leading the combined British and Russian forces in a high-stepping, Anglo-Mongolian knees-up.

Epilogue

AND THUS I leave my Command at our moment of Final Glory when East and West joined hands in Ultimate Victory.

It is with a proud heart and a pricking eye that I have looked back at my Army days when Comradeship flowered in the Forcing-house of War and I was privileged to lead Twelve Platoon, the Fourth Musketeers, the grandest bunch of chaps who ever marched to the beat of the drum. How dearly would I like to see them all again! I have tried every year since demobilization to organize a Platoon Reunion, but, unfortunately, I have never seemed to strike a date and venue which everyone found suitable to their differing commitments.

However, we must look forward as well as back. What with the Cold War, the Space Race, and all this rock-and-roll, it has not been an easy wicket for Britain since 1945. But, as I often tell the lads at the Youth Club, so long as our youngsters remember their Noble Heritage and play a Straight Bat in the Game of Life, they will see the Old Country through just as my generation did before them. If they will but use those simple virtues of grit, pluck, and never-say-die, which it pleases Almighty God to breed in every Britisher, then they will neither be found wanting when the Great Call comes, nor unworthy of their fathers, the Heavily-Armed Civilians of World War II. I am confident that they will rally again to the Flag, look up in defiance as the mushroom cloud foams across the sky, face the nuclear fallout with unflinching courage, and start a fresh page in our Glorious History as the heroic symbols of the New Elizabethan Age, proud to be known as the first of the Heavily Radioactive Civilians.

bw Ryan, Patrick
How I won the war.